Delphi and the Sac...

SOME OTHER BOOKS ABOUT GREECE PUBLISHED BY MICHAEL HAAG

An Affair of the Heart *by Dilys Powell*
The Villa Ariadne *by Dilys Powell*
The Traveller's Journey is Done *by Dilys Powell*
Guide to Greece *by Michael Haag and Neville Lewis*

Send for our complete list:
Michael Haag Limited
PO Box 369
London NW3 4ER
England

DELPHI AND THE SACRED WAY

by Neville Lewis

MICHAEL HAAG

FOR MIRANDA

Delphi and the Sacred Way
© 1987 by
Neville Lewis
Cover design by Colin Elgie
Typeset by Witwell Limited, 92 The Albany,
Old Hall Street, Liverpool L3 9EJ

Printed in Great Britain by litho at the Bath Press,
Lower Bristol Road, Bath BA2 3BL

Published by Michael Haag Limited, PO Box 369,
London NW3 4ER, England

ISBN 0 902743 45 7

Contents

Acknowledgements

This book has few scholarly pretensions but I would like to record my thanks to the scholar and topographer Eugene Vanderpool of the American School of Classical Studies at Athens who in addition to other help once drew for me from memory a detailed map of the area of the Phocicon and the Schist Road and thereby first interested me in its history. I also owe a debt to Eugene Vanderpool Jr for lending me at a critical moment one of his cameras; I only wish that his professional hand had also taken the photographs.

I was greatly assisted by several local historians and savants, particularly Evthymios Dalkas of Levadia, the late Nikos Liberis of Davlia and Athanasios Scopas of Ayia Marina. For their help and that of the countless other individuals who were prepared to answer questions and elaborate stories (even if they were not always to be believed) I am very grateful.

Finally I wish to thank the National Tourist Organisation of Greece for affording me travel facilities in Greece.

Introduction

The Parnassos area, like much of Greece, is most often visited by foreigners on account of one or two major sites — in this case Delphi and the monastery of Osios Loukas. A few people may stop briefly at Levadia, though probably only for a souvlaki; some may pause at the huge marble lion beside the road at Chaironia and others to shop at Arachova. Those a little more familiar with the region might venture across Parnassos to cool Eptalophos or descend below Delphi through the olive groves and along the coast to Galaxidi. Comparatively few visitors stay anywhere other than at Delphi, and most of those who do stay there spend only a night or two before returning to Athens. The vast majority rushes to Delphi and back in one day.

It is a pity. Even apart from Delphi and Osios Loukas there are numerous other places of interest illustrative of practically every aspect of the Greek past and present — all in incomparably magnificent scenery dominated by the great mountain of Parnassos.

This book is an attempt to make the reader linger, if only in the imagination, in this beautiful part of Greece. I believe too that more may be learnt about a country by coming to know well one part of it than by gaining a superficial acquaintance with parts of all of it. For this reason I have sometimes adopted the method of moving from the particular to the general, in an effort to put matters in their proper context. So for example there may be longer sections on the Turkish occupation of Greece or the War of Independence than you would expect to find in a local guide. If any of these prove too long for the reader, they can easily be bypassed if necessary with the help of the index. Inevitably Delphi and Osios Loukas are dealt with at some length owing to their importance but not in the conventional guide book manner — again I have tried to look a little behind the facade.

The text has been supplemented with plans of the sanctuary and the museum at Delphi and of the mosaics of Osios Loukas. These are in the appendices at the end of the book, where there is also an Outline Chronology. In addition there are some travel notes for getting about the area. In the text various walks are described, but it is not assumed that many readers are walkers.

Delphi and the Sacred Way began with my interest in the famous Schist Road, that elusive part of the Sacred Way to Delphi where by tradition Oedipus had killed his father. In the end I became fascinated by the whole Parnassos region. The Sacred Way was of course a road, a road that we shall attempt to follow. It is also more than that, for it can lead anywhere you wish it to go.

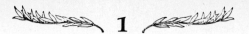

1

THE SACRED WAY

The road from Athens to Delphi was anciently a sacred way. Its route lay via the old cities of Eleusis, Thebes and Levadia. According to one tradition the god Apollo had travelled along it on his mission to civilise mankind. Later there came the processions of the Pythiad which were sent from time to time by the Athenians to sing paeans and to celebrate the god's presence at Delphi. The same road was travelled again by the group of young women from Athens, the Thyiads, who every two years in the autumn went to join the Dionysian revels on Parnassos, pausing on their way to dance the rhythmic dithyramb in honour of Bacchos.

At first the road followed the Sacred Way to Eleusis. This started from the Sacred Gate in the city walls of Athens and having left behind the funerary monuments of the Kerameikos cemetery soon began to mount the ridge of Aigaleos which enclosed the city from the west and where the traveller could obtain a last view of the Acropolis. Then beyond the laurel trees that were subsequently to give their name to the monastery of Daphni the road descended to the shores of the Eleusinian Gulf and crossed the Thriasian Plain to the entrance of the Sanctuary of Demeter in the small township of Eleusis. Today's traffic still travels largely along this ancient route. Much of the way is now bordered by heavy industry, and even the waters of Salamis are often filled with the expensive casualties of modern trade — the ships that have no work. Yet at one time the road was the scene of a great torchlit procession which every September travelled to the Temple of Demeter for the Greater Eleusinia.

At the head of the procession there was carried a statue of Iacchos — or Dionysos. Then came the priests with the sacred objects of the cult hidden from sight in baskets, and finally there was the huge crowd of mystai or initiates. No other festival in Greece was of more consequence or surrounded with greater secrecy. Only those initiated earlier at the Lesser Eleusinia at Athens could take part in the procession, and a further stage of initiation was necessary at Eleusis before they could attend the Mysteries. These took place in the Telesterion, a square windowless building arranged with tiers of seats on either side to accommodate some 3000 people. We can only speculate as to what occurred: it may have involved a dramatic representation of the union of Zeus and Demeter (which produced Kore or Persephone), or even of the communion of men with their gods after death, since some glimpse of a blissful future reserved for the mystai was apparently given them which was more comforting than the traditional picture of a shadowy existence in the Underworld.

Many travellers to Delphi would know little of the Mysteries. Their purpose was to seek communion with the gods of Delphi in a different and more direct manner.

Beyond Eleusis were the wooded hills of Cithairon, where below the pass of the Oak's Heads into Boeotia the fortress of Eleutherai guarded the frontier of Attica. At the summit of the pass the travellers and processions would have stopped, before descending to Erythrai, to look across the Boeotian plains to the dark grey rim of Parnassos in the northwest. So the Thyiads must have done when late on a warm October day the fourteen young women arrived as if on the edge of a new world and thought nervously of the time when possessed by the god they would run over the mountain in a frenzied search for a victim. Perhaps they now performed one of their first dances, revolving in a circle by the roadside and remembering that it was here on Cithairon that the Bacchants had torn Pentheus limb from limb.

The view from Cithairon was then only a little different from today. The mountains are now more blasted, more bony, and there is no glint of light on the shallow water of the Copais lake now that the marsh has gone. Yet especially on such a day in early autumn Boeotia has a primitive rawness in its shades of browns and yellow and gold that belongs to some basic unchanging pattern and recalls an endless sequence of unbroken seasons stretching back to the infancy of man.

*

The Boeotian plains lie cradled within a ring of mountains which can be described as the lineal descendants of the Pindos range, that great wall that divides continental Greece down its centre and forms the backbone of Roumeli. South of the Pindos the mountains of Aitolia press against the waters of the Corinthian Gulf and the line as if deflected continues eastwards from Giona through

Parnassos, Helicon, Cithairon and Parnes while a more northerly limb branches out from Oiti along the Euboean Gulf through Kallidromon, Clomon and Ptoon until in a gentle refrain it completes the circuit of Boeotia. So enclosed are these fertile fields that the streams which find their way into them from the higher ground are mostly unable to flow out towards the sea except by way of katavothras or swallow-holes through the limestone. The river Cephisos for example, which rises above the small plain of ancient Doris and then flows along the valley between Kallidromon and Parnassos, for centuries used to feed the marshes of Lake Copais; in winter the lake would swell, and in spring and summer it slowly drained away through the natural outlets in the surrounding hills, so that much of its area could then be cultivated or grazed.

The fertility of the soil and the position of Boeotia at the cross-roads of continental Greece, together with the comparatively easy access to the sea both at the Corinthian Gulf and the Gulf of Euboea, assisted the emergence of two great cities in the Mycenaean period, namely Thebes and Orchomenos. Each city dominated one of the two basins into which the Boeotian plain naturally divides, Thebes controlling the southern half and Orchomenos ruling the Copaic basin to the north. There was intense rivalry between the two, and periodic warfare. In the Mycenaean period Orchomenos was generally the more important, while after the Dorian invasions Thebes became the stronger and eventually assumed the leadership of the federation of Boeotian cities during the classical period. In the fourth century the Thebans twice destroyed the city of their old rivals.

The situation of the Boeotian isthmus at the centre of mainland Greece gave it a still wider significance. Every invading army coming south by land had to travel this way, and two of the most important battles in antiquity were fought at either end of it. In 338 BC at Chaironia, where the valley of the Cephisos opens into the Boeotian plain, Philip of Macedon defeated the Greek army and won control of Greece. And below the passes over Cithairon, at Plataia, in 479 BC an allied Greek army succeeded in routing the Persians and finally — or at least for some two thousand years — denied the attempt by the East to bring Greece within its orbit.

The Sacred Way, having descended Cithairon, passed a few kilometres to the east of the small city of Plataia in front of which that great issue was decided. A short way ahead, beyond a line of low hills, lies Thebes. That once great city is now a provincial town like many another, little more than a museum of memories for any visitor, as it is almost totally bereft of tangible remains of its past. Shortly after the battle of Chaironia, Alexander levelled every house in the city except that of the poet Pindar. By the reign of the Roman emperor Augustus Thebes was not even the size of a respectable village, and 150 years later the traveller Pausanias found only the Cadmea, the ancient acropolis, to be inhabited while a solitary statue stood among the ruins of the former market place. Today the only prominent monument is the solitary tower that remains from the Frankish castle which was once the proud home of the Duchy of Athens in the thirteenth century. This stands next to the archaeological museum at the northern end of the former acropolis.

The way to Delphi is dogged by the memory of Oedipus, the tragic king of Thebes. As a baby Oedipus had been exposed to die on Mount Cithairon. In manhood after unwittingly killing his father on the Schist Road he became king at Thebes by solving the famous riddle of the Sphinx. You pass the Mountain of the Sphinx (or the Sphingion Oros, as it is still called) shortly after leaving Thebes on the road to Levadia. The height lies to the right, stark and menacing, and when seen from the west it does have something of the appearance of the monster, with the outline of a woman's face and the outstretched paws of a lion. Here the creature had lived, so the story went, devouring those travellers along the road who could not answer the question, 'What is it that walks on four legs in the morning, on two at noon, and three in the evening?'. When Oedipus gave the correct answer, 'Man', the Sphinx in her fury threw herself from the mountain and Oedipus was then hailed by the Thebans as their saviour and their king.

*

The road to Levadia, still following the line of the Sacred Way, leaves the Theban plain by rising over the furthest spurs of Helicon and then passes the remains of the ancient city of Haliartos. Standing on higher ground between the waters of the Copais and the mountain behind, the city once commanded the pass between the two plains of Boeotia. Its acropolis stood on a low rocky hill some 15 metres above the lake which stretched away to the north. Nowadays in autumn, when the cotton plants are still in flower showing a dull un-Mediterranean white across the wide plain as far as the foothills of Mount Clomon, it is difficult to bring to mind the former lake or rather seasonal swamp which throughout the historic period covered much of the plain of Orchomenos and from which was harvested not so much cotton as especially palatable eels. As the area was only drained permanently at the end of the last century there is no shortage of descriptions of its former appearance. JG Frazer in his *Commentary on Pausanias* described it in winter: 'Viewed from a height such as the acropolis of Orchomenos it appeared as an immense fen, of a vivid green colour, stretching away for miles and miles, overgrown with sedge, reeds and canes, through which the river Cephisus or Melas might be seen sluggishly oozing, while here and there a gleam of sunlit water, especially towards the northeast of the mere, directed the eye to what looked like ponds in the vast green swamp. Bare grey mountains rising on the north and east, and the beautiful wooded slopes of Helicon on the south, bounded the fen'.†

There remained a tradition preserved by the ancient geographer Strabo that at a much earlier period the area had been drained and cultivated by the Orchomenians, whose power and wealth Pausanias also speaks of at a time prior to the Trojan War. The modern drainage works have demonstrated the truth of part of the tradition, for they have revealed a complete system of ancient dykes and canals which were designed to take the water directly to the natural outlets on the eastern side of the plain. The importance of Orchomenos during the Mycenaean period and the existence of the remarkable fortress of Gla near the principal area of the katavothras certainly suggest that the Orchomenians were indeed responsible for draining the entire basin at that stage. Yet by the time of Homer it was once again a lake, and for this another tradition in literature may provide the explanation. Pausanias records a Theban story that their hero Heracles had blocked up 'the chasm through the mountain' and had diverted the Cephisos into the plain. In fact one of the principal katavothras in the northeast was found to have been blocked by large rocks, thereby causing the plain to be flooded. Whether the blocking of the outlet occurred by natural means such as an earthquake or by act of war, the Thebans would have been proud to claim responsibility for their hero Heracles.

†Vol. V, p. 112

Though the lake then remained for some three thousand years or more a permanent seasonal feature with the embankments of the old canals serving as causeways through the swamp, some memory always survived among the local inhabitants that recalled a time when the plain was dry. In the 1870s, well before the area was finally drained and the full extent of the ancient canal system known, there was this story told by the peasants of Boeotia. An old king once ruled over the whole plain, which was at that time dry since it was drained by katavothras. The king had two sons. To one he gave his lands and to the other his herds. When a severe frost and snowstorm destroyed all the animals their owner asked his brother for a share in the land. The wealthy brother turned him away, and the herdsman avenged himself by stopping up the katavothras. The lake rose, the land flooded and all the villagers were submerged under the waves. Here the heroic struggle between two great cities has gone, and in its place we find a version of a similar story which is more suitable to the humble affairs of a latter-day Greece.

*

The road continues to skirt the southern margin of the plain just as it did in the long days of the marsh, and it is towards the modern town of Levadia, anciently Lebadea, that it now bends. But as the way turns past Mount Laphystion, first look across the fields towards the site of Orchomenos. The ancient city lay on the lower slopes of Akontion, 'the Javelin', a long ridge that here launches itself out into the plain. The eastern end of Akontion provided a strong position for a settlement where it could control both the land around it and the passes into Boeotia from not only the valley of the Cephisos but also from Phocis and Delphi; the site was almost continuously occupied from the Neolithic through to the Hellenistic period. The highest point of the hill is still dominated by a keep-like acropolis built in the fourth century BC in the finest style of military architecture comparable with Messene and Eleutherai. Below this can be seen the city walls, which ran down the north and south sides of the hill to join a third section on the east near the level ground, thus forming a roughly triangular enclosure around the Hellenic and Macedonian cities with the acropolis at the apex. However despite its restoration by Philip of Macedon after the battle of Chaironia the city soon disappeared into the same pale obscurity as its enemy Thebes. One great monument does survive from the earlier period when Orchomenos had not yet been humbled by Thebes. That is the 'Treasury of Minyas', excavated by Schliemann in the 1880s. The revenues of the legendary king Minyas were so large according to Pausanias that they required a treasury to receive them. The 'treasury' that Pausanias described as being no less marvellous than the Pyramids of Egypt is, like the so-called 'Treasury of Atreus' at Mycenae, a large beehive tomb and of very similar size; it probably predates that at Mycenae by about one hundred years. The tomb contains two chambers, the smaller of which has a ceiling of pale greenish schist carved in low relief with a beautiful pattern of rosettes, spirals and a sort of palmette. It is situated not far from the ancient theatre, across the road from the church of the Koimisis.

If you do go to Orchomenos you should also visit the church of the Koimisis, itself a remarkable structure. It belonged to the monastery of the Koimisis tis Theotokou (Assumption of the Virgin Mary) founded in 874 by Leo, the then steward to the Byzantine emperor. As can be seen the church was mostly built of ancient materials, probably from the sanctuary of the Graces mentioned by Pausanias. The particular interest of the building is that it is the earliest example in Greece of the domed cross-in-square church which superseded the aisled basilical form developed in antiquity. Here the Greek cross, formed by the nave, the transepts and the apse, is not fully developed and is superimposed upon what is fundamentally the scheme of a basilica. Moreover the dome has been placed directly on the walls at the intersection of the four arms of the cross without any of the devices developed in later churches to resolve the square ground plan more happily into the circular dome above it. Nevertheless this is the first phase of the form which was to achieve maturity barely a century later in the magnificent structures of Daphni and Osios Loukas.

2

OMORPHI LEVADIA

We left the Thyiads behind us as they looked over the Boeotian plains from Cithairon. Pausanias tells us that they stopped to dance at several places on their way to Delphi. One of those places must have been Thebes, where the Theban reed-flute would mark their steps. Across the border into Phocis they stopped too at Panopeos (Ayios Vlasios), 'of the beautiful dancing-places'. And another break in their journey would probably have come at Lebadea, now Levadia. The ancient road having rounded the northwesterly extension of Helicon then forded the waters of the Hercyna at Lebadea much as it does today, and it would have been a natural place to stop midway between Thebes and Delphi.

The modern town (which occupies roughly the same position as the Hellenic city) is situated at the foot of the northern spurs of Helicon, at the entrance of a great ravine which penetrates deep into the mountain and from which the river Hercyna issues. On either side of this fast-flowing stream the houses climb up the sides of the two hills that enclose Levadia, Varthavitsa to the southeast and Ayios Elias to the west. A large mediaeval castle guards a rocky height at the back of the town. With its varying levels, and the two faces of the city meeting in the middle and spilling over into the plain below it, Levadia is still attractive enough, especially when seen from the north. At one time, before its almost total ruin in the first year of the War of Independence, when it was one of the most important cities in Roumeli and could be described by one traveller as presenting a 'gay assemblance of mosques, minarets, houses and gardens', then indeed Levadia was omorphi or beautiful. It is to that time that the song refers:

> Beautiful — that's Levadia,
> With its houses so high
> And balconies so fine.
> Indoors they play the violin,
> And out of doors they dance.

Much of that charm has gone for ever, but it remains a place where you can linger a little.

In the past much of the prosperity of Levadia depended on those waters of the Hercyna which made Levadia not only a garden city but drove the wheels of numerous mills. In the seventeenth century George Wheler observed that the river 'cometh with such a plentiful source out of the mountain by the castle that it turneth 20 mills in the Town, not a Bowshot off its rise'.† The mills crushed the wheat and rice that fed much of central Greece and they fulled the woollen clothes manufactured in the region. In addition Levadia was (and still is) the centre of trade in the agricultural products of the region; it was the home of wealthy merchants who not only dealt in the local produce and even fixed the prices of such goods for a large part of Greece but exported many of them abroad to Italy and even England — cotton, olive oil, corn, currant raisins and prinari (a red dye). The merchant families enjoyed under the Turks positions hardly inferior to the Moslems, ruling the territory as magistrates, collecting taxes and farming land through their Christian tenants. Leake who visited Levadia not long before the War of Independence wrote, 'Levadia has a greater air of opulence than any place in North Greece — partly in consequence of the small number of Turks who generally are not only poor themselves but a cause of poverty in others, and partly the effect of the larger Greek houses shown to advantage on the steep declivity of the hill'.‡ Practically every visitor was struck by the spaciousness of the houses — the houses which disappeared under ashes in 1821.

More recently it has been one particular product, vamvaki or cotton, which has underpinned the economy of Levadia. Many of the population are farmers who daily go out to their fields in the plain where cotton is the main crop. Several large factories have been built — mills to gin the cotton, spin the yarn and weave the cloth, although for these the energy of the Hercyna is no longer necessary. Now too, as the capital of the nome or county of Viotia (Boeotia), Levadia remains a busy regional centre. The narrow dusty streets echo with the sound of the passing crowd, and the faded buildings which have been thrown together, new and old, tiled and concreted, in inelegant confusion appear animated by the bustle around them.

† *Journey into Greece* (1682), p. 326
‡ *Travels in Northern Greece* (1835), Vol. II, p. 118

*

The buses from Athens to Delphi usually stop by the practoreio or agency housed in a restaurant opposite some empty gardens in the plateia of Labros Katsonis. The street where the agency is situated, Odhos Bouphidou, continues past the traffic island to become one of the main shopping streets and leads directly to the central Plateia Georgiou A' (King George I). Here you find the National Bank, several kafeneions, a hotel and in the vicinity a number of small restaurants. Above this main square, near the post office and the Demarcheion or Town Hall there is another smaller plateia with a

Levadia: making phyllo

garden. From this relatively high point in the town you obtain a fine view of Parnassos with its great grey ridges and of the cleft with neighbouring Mount Cirphis. Nearer at hand the most conspicuous feature apart from the kastro is the large clock tower standing out from the surrounding houses on the side of a hill. This tower, built originally by the Franks, at one time housed a clock which Lord Elgin gave to the town in 1803. 'O Elgin mas gelase', a clerk at the Town Hall once said to me: 'Elgin made a fool of us; he gave with one hand and took with the other'. For the Greeks nothing Elgin did can be right, but in this case Levadia gained from the exchange. The clock was given in return for official approval of his proposed excavations of the oracle of Trophonius, and the search proved as fruitless as it was at Orchomenos where his workmen had been unable to dig out the Treasury of Minyas owing to the size of the stones blocking the way. And it was above Lord Elgin's clock that the flag of the revolution was to fly in 1821.

To reach the springs of the Hercyna you initially proceed in the direction of the clock tower. First you cross Plateia George I into Odhos Venizelou where you turn right into Odhos Lappa and cross the river. Above the stream stands the modest Hotel Hercyna looking as if at any moment it might crumble away and be dragged by the enveloping vegetation into the foaming water below. Odhos Lappa then joins a narrow street that runs at right angles, named Odhos Strategou Ioannou; opposite the junction some steps lead towards the clock tower and a number of attractive old houses. We are now on the west bank of the Hercyna and the older houses of Levadia are all on this side. Though few of the buildings predate the burning of the town in 1821 (and Odhos Strategou Ioannou dates almost entirely from the subsequent rebuilding) some retain features copied from the Turks like the wooden loggia or gallery, and it is clear that during the Turkish period Levadia was mostly concentrated on these slopes of Ayios Elias on the west of the river where the mediaeval kastro had also been built previously. The ancient city had it seems lain chiefly on the other side of the river, where even in the nineteenth century the traveller William Mure observed 'numerous fragments of antiquity still scattered over the eminence', and perhaps for that reason the later townships had risen on the freer space on the western bank. However the modern town has gradually spread over the east bank also and all obvious traces of ancient Lebadea have long since disappeared.

The square at the top of Odhos Ioannou is the Plateia Diakou and it is our immediate destination. Here where the sound of water becomes noticeable it is only a short distance to the springs of the Hercyna as well as to the kastro above them. This area was at one time the centre of the old Turkish town and it was here that the weekly bazaar was held, where the farmers brought their produce and the merchants fixed the prices. The place is quieter now, except for the occasional coach-load of visitors. To one side of the square is the large Metropolitan church of the Panagia, the seat of the Bishop of Thebes and Levadia, which was built in 1859 in place of a former mosque where in 1677 Spon and Wheler had seen the inscriptions confirming (if confirmation was needed) that Levadia was indeed ancient Lebadea.

At the top of the plateia there is a bust of the hero Thanasios Diakos after whom the square was named. Diakos was the military leader of eastern Greece at the beginning of the War of Independence but was captured at the battle of Alamana in 1821 and then killed by the Turks in a particularly cruel manner. The inscription is based upon that by the poet Palamas on the cenotaph at Lamia, and it reads like this:

> And the pride of heroes
> in the glory of our Lord
> brought you, Thanasis Diakos,
> the suffering of martyrdom.

In fact Diakos was roasted alive on a spit, surrounded by the heads of the Greek dead, one of which was that of Isaias the Bishop of Salona.

*

The story of Diakos and Isaias deserves to be retold in some detail because it concerns the outset of the War of Independence in Roumeli, and in this Levadia played an important part. However the revolution against the Turks came at the end of many centuries of foreign occupation of which the Turkish was only the longest and the last. One of the strangest episodes of all is the period of Catalan rule.

When the great city of Constantinople, which had ruled Greece as part of the Byzantine Empire since the division of the ancient world in AD 395, was sacked by the Fourth Crusade in 1204, most of Greece was divided into a number of Frankish principalities, one of which was the Duchy of Athens with its capital at Thebes. There remained a Byzantine ruler in Epiros and the emperor himself succeeded in recapturing Constantinople in 1261, but central Greece was never again within the territories of Byzantium. The empire had at least served to perpetuate a common Greek culture of a kind, but now Greece was in the hands of total foreigners for over six hundred years.

Early in the fourteenth century the Duchy of Athens passed into the hands of Walter de Brienne. It was as a consequence of the Duke's ambitions against Byzantine territory that the Catalan Grand Company comes to have a place in the history of Levadia. The Grand Company was a body of Spanish mercenaries from Catalonia and Aragon enlisted by the Sicilians to fight against the French. After the twenty years of the Sicilian War another role was found for them in the services of the Byzantine emperor Andronicus. Andronicus faced a new threat from the east in the form of the growing power of the Turks, and in particular the Othman Turks. His policy was to employ mercenaries and he accepted the offer of Roger de Flor, a German-Italian adventurer, together with a body of the Spanish troops. In 1303 Roger arrived at Constantinople with six thousand men and was appointed commander of the army in Asia Minor.

This is how the historian Finlay described the subsequent impact of the Catalans upon the Byzantine empire: 'They came and departed as if under the guidance of the destroying angel. In daring courage, steady discipline, and military skill, they were not surpassed by any Greek or Roman army. Their warlike deeds entitled them to rank as a host of heroes; their individual acts made them a band of demons. They had proved invincible on every field of battle... Guided by a sovereign like Leo III or like Basil II they might have conquered the Seljouk Turks, strangled the Ottoman power in its cradle... but Andronicus could neither make us of their valour, nor secure their obedience. His own senseless intrigues roused their hostile feelings; and after they had made every tribe in the Seljouk empire tremble for a moment they turned back on the Greek empire, where they carried on their ravages with a degree of cruelty and rapacity which history cannot attempt to portray'.†
After defeating the emperor the Spaniards then moved into Thrace

†History of Greece, Vol. III, p. 388

which they plundered for two years before moving into the richer pastures of Macedonia.

In 1309 the Catalans finally left Byzantine territory and entered into the service of Walter de Brienne, the Duke of Athens and Thebes, but Walter was no more successful in employing them than Andronicus. When the Spaniards were finally owed large arrears of pay they turned against their masters. In the spring of 1311 the Duke of Athens together with the ruler of Salona, Thomas d'Autremencourt, and the Marquis of Bodonitsa and indeed the entire Frankish chivalry of Greece rode into Boeotia to deal once and for all with these recalcitrant mercenaries. The Franks established their camp at the tower which still stands on Mount Thourion. In the plain below, before Scripou (Orchomenos), there stood the Catalan footmen. It should have been an easy matter for the heavily armoured knights to ride down on the men on foot and crush them beneath the weight of their attack. But some unnamed commander on the Spanish side had as the hero Heracles once did diverted the Cephisos into the fields, creating a green mire which from above appeared like the pleasant meadows of the French countryside. Into this with banners aloft the duke and his knights rode, and then sank ignobly into the mud, where standing like statues they were cut down by the lances and knives of the Catalans. Walter de Brienne was killed along with every single Frankish knight — except two, who were captured. The period of Frankish rule in central Greece was at an end. The Catalans had only to walk into Levadia and after the destruction of the Frankish fortress at Thebes make themselves masters of Boeotia and Attica. Levadia became their foremost military position, and it was probably they who built the large castle there as well as many of the square towers to be seen in the region.

Strangely enough the Catalans did not govern themselves. Initially one of the two captives from the battle of Scripou, a French knight called Roger Deslau, was asked to take command. This he wisely did for a time before advising the Spaniards to obtain the services of a real prince while he retired to the castle of Salona (Amphissa) as its ruler. Finally in 1326 the son of the King of Sicily was made the duke of the Catalan territory which now extended to Neo-Patras (Ipati) in the south of Thessaly. Thus for about sixty years central Greece came to be ruled by the Sicilians, but was held on their behalf by the Catalans.

*

The Catalan castle is still largely intact despite being badly damaged in an earthquake in 1894. It is approached most easily from the Odhos Phrouriou which runs up at right angles to the Hercyna, as you walk from the Plateia Diakou towards the sources of the river. A large tower stands close to the water and above it the north wall of the castle ascends the side of the hill. On three sides the outer ward of the castle needed no more defence than that given by the cliffs above the gorge of the Hercyna; only on the fourth side, the north, were walls added. From the Odhos Phrouriou a path leads to a fine double gateway in the north wall, and from this point to the further extent of the walls to the west double walls protected the castle from the direction in which it was most exposed to attack. Inside the gateway the path mounts through pines and cypresses to a ruinous entrance into the inner ward which is guarded by a huge tower.

At the southwest corner of this inner defence there is a small building dating from the same period as the castle and now comprising two chapels placed one above the other. On the upper floor is Ayia Sophia, while the older chapel below it is dedicated to Ayia Varvara. The church of Ayia Varvara, built above a cistern that provided water for the castle, was of particular importance to the Catalans. Here was deposited the skull of Saint George, the protector of the house of Aragon where it stayed under permanent guard. The rulers of the house of Aragon despite many efforts could never obtain the skull from the Spaniards at Levadia, and there it remained until after a period in Aegina the relic finally went to Venice in the fifteenth century.

*

The castle of Levadia was to assume what many Greeks would consider a far greater significance in 1821, but over four hundred years of foreign rule had still to pass before then. The Turks occupied central Greece for most of that time. Yet their arrival was neither particularly sudden nor unexpected. The acquisition by the Turks of the territories of the former Byzantine Empire occurred over a great many years, and was not always unwelcome to inhabitants who were as oppressed in the east by the Byzantine officials as they were in the west by their feudal overlords. Gibbon when commenting on the petty tyrants that disputed Greece after 1204 went so far as to say, 'if servitude be preferable to anarchy [the Greeks] might repose with joy under the Turkish yoke'.†

Towards the end of the fourteenth century the Sultan Bayezid marched into Thessaly. By this time the Catalans had made way in their turn for the Florentine Nerio Acciaioli who had become master of Athens, Thebes and Levadia by 1387. The Bishop of Phocis invited the Turks to conquer Greece, but after occupying Levadia in 1394 and advancing into the Peloponnese they retired back to Thessaly. The Sultan was content to allow members of Nerio's family to rule the Duchy as vassals of the Ottoman empire, until finally in 1456 — three years after the capture of Constantinople — the more ambitious Sultan Mehmet II took Athens and then Levadia.

And so began over three and a half centuries of Sklavia or Slavery, as the Greeks call the period of Turkish occupation. The term is of course an exaggeration, at least as a description of the last 150 years where we have accounts of the country from the various Western travellers. However oppressed some sections of the population remained (most obviously the peasant farmers), many Greeks came to have a dominant role not only within their own country but in the Ottoman empire at large. What is at first surprising is that those Greeks occupying the most prominent positions were later in the vanguard of the revolution against the Turks.

The essence of the Turkish administration was taxation. Without doubt this was heavy and oppressive to the Greeks. Their produce, their cattle, even their persons were taxed. Initially the Moslems imposed a tribute on Christian children, taking one in five to become Janissaries, the key soldiers·and administrators of the Ottoman empire. Both the haratch or capitation tax and the child-tribute could be avoided by any Christian who embraced Islam. The temptations to apostasy were great and the numbers who succumbed remarkably small. The detestable system of child-tribute stopped before the end of the seventeenth century but not before the practice had encouraged, as did the whole fiscal system, the widespread use of deceit as the best weapon against extortion and had helped form those qualities in the Greeks which Patrick Leigh Fermor has elaborated under the name of Romaiosune in his book *Roumeli*.

†*Decline and Fall*, Vol. VII, p. 384

The collection of these taxes was often farmed out to the leaders of the Greek communities, who thus became the agents of their Turkish masters and of the whole oppressive system. In this way the Greek primates obtained considerable local power. Levadia is a good case in point. Before 1821 it formed part of the pashalik of Egriboz (Euboea, Boeotia, Locris and Attica) and was governed by a voivoda appointed by the Porte (the Turkish government at Constantinople) whose duty it was to collect its revenues earmarked for the administration of the royal mosques. The Turkish governor then let the collection of the taxes to the three Greek archons or magistrates of the town, who together with the clergy exercised the civil and judicial administration over the Greek inhabitants. In effect Levadia and the territory around it enjoyed a large amount of self-government.

The archons themselves were wealthy men who further profited from the taxes they collected. Colonel Leake who visited Levadia shortly before the War of Independence spoke of the sorry state of the Greek peasant even on land held by his fellow Christians. 'To complete his misery' the traveller continues, 'the upper class of Greeks of Levadia are as insolent and unfeeling to their inferiors as they are malignantly jealous of one another, though they have all the hospitality, wit and sociable disposition of the nation.'† This judgment by Leake and also many of the comments of Finlay and other travellers of the eighteenth and nineteenth centuries on the character of the Greeks must be seen in the context of their surprise and disappointment at not finding an up-to-date version of their conception of the ancient Greeks. At Levadia their surprise was indeed great when they encountered these Turko-Christians dressed in the Turkish manner, living in large houses with servants, 'the servile imitators of their superiors', full of pretensions and yet with 'barbarous' and 'disgusting' manners. The picture is certainly exaggerated, and many travellers had nothing but compliments to pay the primates for the manner of their reception at Levadia. Nonetheless it is the case that as large a gap existed between the Greek or Albanian peasant and the Greek upper classes as between the peasant and his Turkish masters.

One man who seems to have met with almost universal approval was Ioannis Logothetis who became archon of Levadia before 1800 and was still an archon in 1821. He had early established himself as

† *Travels in Northern Greece* (1835), Vol. II, p. 202

Ioannis Logothetis, archon of Levadia

a rich trader and farmer, and by 1804 had built a huge house for himself with a household of over fifty persons. Excessive wealth usually attracted Turkish avarice, and indeed Ioannis' brother had been sufficiently indiscreet in this respect as to be decapitated at Constantinople and his possessions seized by the Sultan. Logothetis' house deserved to be called a palace according to one visitor, yet he was able to deceive the Turks by only ever receiving them in a room with the barest amount of furniture. Despite his enormous wealth Logothetis met with the favour not only of the many travellers he entertained (including Byron and Hobhouse in 1809) but also of his fellow Greeks. He was just and he was generous. The lands which he rented from the Turks he relet at only moderate rents. His door was open to anyone, his doctor was available for the sick and his table for the poor — so history relates. He was also a patriot. When in 1813 the Englishmen Hughes and Cockerell were entertained by the archon, they drank together a toast to King George of England and also to the liberty of the Greeks. Later Logothetis became a member of the Philiki Hetairia and was deeply involved in the events of 1821.

Besides this local magistracy which existed in many places under the Turks, the other important institution within Greece was the church. For all its apparent venality and despite the ignorance and bigotry of much of the clergy, the church as the guardian of the Orthodox religion remained the focus of a nationalism often identified with the Orthodox faith. Also the church kept alive the written form of the Greek language, even if this developed as an over-elaborate imitation of the language of the Fathers of the Church. In addition the church was both wealthy and powerful. The Greeks preferred to give their lands to the monasteries than have them occupied by the Turks, and the Moslems found it easier to allow the existing institution of the church to act in a judicial capacity in the manner of the Moslem kadi (judge) than to invent a different form of administration. Thus Christians took their legal disputes to their Bishops to decide according to the Roman law.

At Constantinople the Patriarch (the head of the Orthodox church) exercised a secular authority, advising the Sultan and indeed acting himself in relation to the affairs of the Christian subjects of the Ottoman Empire. The important position secured by the Orthodox hierarchy as well as by the Fanariots (the Greeks of the capital) in the administration and commerce of the empire served to encourage the continuing belief in the eventual restoration of the Byzantine Empire, with a Christian emperor once more on the throne at Constantinople. When by a conjunction of events the war commenced against the Turks in 1821 the church hierarchy placed itself in the forefront, since the Greeks saw themselves fighting a holy war against the Moslems.

Although Levadia enjoyed a large measure of self-government, there was a substantial Turkish minority within its population. In other places, some nearby, there were no Turks at all. Arachova and Desphina are examples. Kastri (Delphi), then a wretchedly poor village, had only very few Turks. As a rule there was a great difference between the mountain and the plain. The Turks controlled the plains but left the mountains almost entirely to the Greeks, where in some places the use of local Christian militias (the armatoli) was sanctioned, and in others there was no authority at all beyond that of the bands of klephts or bandits who exacted contributions from the villages and preyed off the Turks whenever they could.

The armatoli and klephts were but the counterpart of each other; the armatoli were necessary to control the klephts, and the klephts provided many of the recruits for the armatoliks. In time practically every area of northern Greece had armatoliks, including even a town on the plain like Levadia. However in the unsettled times at the end of the eighteenth century the number of klephts was greatly increased by the many discontented armatoli. This was partly due to the activities of Ali Pasha of Ioannina. This local potentate was creating in central and western Greece virtually an independent state within the Turkish empire (collecting for example large additional financial levies from Levadia) and he sought to control the armatoliks by introducing Albanian Moslem mercenaries among them, thereby displacing the Greeks. A large body of men under arms thus existed, some owing nominal allegiance to the Turks or to Ali Pasha, and many owing allegiance to no one but themselves, who might one day provide the raw material for an uprising against the foreign masters of Greece.

Among such klepht-armatoli were the Androutsaioi, father and son, and Athanasios Diakos. The older Androutsos is the subject of many klephtica (songs about the klephts), indeed of more than his better known son. One of his celebrated exploits occurred in about 1790. At that time many Greeks were looking to the Orthodox throne of Russia for the restoration of the Byzantine Empire. As with all hopes placed in the intervention of the European powers the Greeks were to be cruelly disappointed until the very last stages of the War of Independence. The Levadite Labros Katsonis, who for many years was in the Russian service, in 1788 at the time of the Russo-Turkish war was given command of a small naval squadron in the Mediterranean to act against the Turkish fleet and the Turkish garrisons ashore. This was to be the signal for an uprising by the Greeks, but in the end nothing came of it. Despite considerable initial successes which encouraged Androutsos and his klephts to join him, Katsonis was defeated in 1790 by the Turkish admiral and only narrowly escaped with his life. Peace between Turkey and Russia spelt the end of his courageous crusade.

Androutsos then remained for some time in the Mani (which was never under Turkish control) but was eventually captured in Dalmatia by the Venetians when on his way to see Katsonis in Russia; he was later handed over to the Turks and put to death at Constantinople (in 1797).

One demotic song concerns the time when Androutsos had left the mountains to join Katsonis. It is one of the finest of the klephtica.

The dark mountains weep, and no comfort is for them.
They weep not for their barren peaks nor weep they for their snow,
But the klephtic band is gone and descends upon the plain.
Giona calls to Liacoura, Liacoura calls in turn:
'Oh Mountain, higher yet than I, whose eyes see further still,
Where are they then, Androutsos and his men?
Where do they turn their spits, where fire they at their mark?
What hills do they adorn with heads of Turkomen?'

'What may I tell you, Mountain friend, what can I say to you?
The parched fields below give welcome to our men.
Amidst the plains turn they their spits and fire they at their mark,
The plains they do adorn with heads of Turkomen.'

Liacoura, when this he heard, most angry he became.
Looking left and looking right, he looks down upon the plain:
'You sickly plain with fields that bring men plague,
Do you demand to be adorned with all my youthful band?
Give back the jewels of my domain, give back the fine young men,
Lest I should melt my slopes of snow and make the fields a sea.'

*

However it was the next generation which would carry arms in the final struggle against the Turks, chief among whom in the region of Levadia were the younger Androutsos and Thanasis Diakos. Odysseus Androutsos having lost his father as a young boy had become a page in the household of Ali Pasha at Ioannina. There he seems to have learnt all the vices of his master. 'His character,' wrote the historian Thomas Gordon, 'was a compound of the Greek and Albanian, with the evil qualities of both prominently displayed, without that respect for their faith which is almost universal among the former race... Bloodthirsty, vindictive, and treacherous as an Arnaut (Albanian), Odysseus surpassed in subtlety and falsehood the most mendacious Greek; he was endowed with an uncommon share of finesse and sagacity, and could at pleasure put on the semblance of virtue. His personal courage was doubtful, and his mistrust excessive, in so much that he did not disclose where he intended to sleep. With regard to bodily qualifications, he had a robust and vigorous constitution, an imposing presence, and incredible swiftness of foot, having more than once outstripped a horse in running...'† When he grew up Odysseus had won the favour of Ali Pasha to such an extent that in 1816 Ali made him the captain of armatoli at Levadia, which by then was under Ali's control. Thanasis Diakos who had earlier been a klepht was appointed Odysseus' protopallikar or lieutenant. Another of Odysseus' officers was Vasilis Bousgos.

In about 1818 Odysseus and Diakos were sworn into the Philiki Hetairia. This secret society had been founded in about 1815, at a time when the Ottoman empire was in decline and many Greeks were affected by the liberal ideas that were sweeping Europe. The object of the society was an armed uprising against the Turks, and many leading Greeks — primates, klephts, merchants and clergy alike — eventually joined. At Levadia Ioannis Logothetis and the other two archons soon followed Odysseus and Diakos as members. However Odysseus' membership of the Hetairia became complicated by his loyalty to Ali Pasha. In the spring of 1820 the Turks began to move against Ali, who in an attempt to make use of the proposed Greek uprising (of which he had some knowledge) as a tactic in his war with the Sultan ordered Odysseus to start an insurrection at Levadia. This policy was strongly opposed by the other Hetairists who knew what it was likely to mean for the city. Finally, when Diakos and Odysseus had quarrelled and the majority of the armatoli had sided with Diakos, Odysseus was forced to leave the post he had been given by Ali; he slipped away to Ithaca where he stayed until the outbreak of the revolution the following year. Diakos was then given the command of the

†*History of the Greek Revolution* (1832), Vol. I, p. 404f

armatolik which he held for the succeeding months until he became the first commander of the revolutionary forces in eastern Greece.

In 1820 and early 1821 the state of Greece was such that many awaited the revolution but no one was certain exactly when and where it was to start. Alexandros Ipsilantis, an officer in the Russian army and one of the leading members of the Hetairia, was anxious to take advantage of the preoccupation of the Ottomans with Ali Pasha and had hoped to begin the revolution in the Morea at the end of 1820. However this was abandoned when at one point it seemed that the Hetairia had been betrayed to the Turks, and instead Ipsilantis decided on beginning the war in the Principalities of Moldavia and Wallachia north of the Danube; here it was possible that Russia might come in against any Turkish intervention. One of the dates canvassed for the uprising in Greece was 6 April, to follow upon Ipsilantis' military campaign in the north, but early in 1821 considerable uncertainty still existed as to his intentions. The leaders of the Morea temporised and wished to postpone the fateful moment until they had further word from St Petersburg.

On 5 March Ipsilantis did cross into Moldavia but communications were such that no news of this reached southern Greece until the end of the month. The campaign in the Principalities turned out to be a fiasco though it helped to distract the Turks, but events in the Morea and Roumeli seem nonetheless to have largely followed the original plan. In the Morea, although some Turks had been killed in remote areas before the end of March, the outbreak of the revolution only occurred after news had come from Moldavia. Then events moved largely under their own impetus; the people took up arms without waiting for any official call from the bishops and primates. The Mani rose on 2 April, Kalavrita fell on that day or the next, and Kalamata on 4 April. According to Greek tradition Bishop Germanos of Patras raised the standard of revolution at the monastery of Ayia Lavra near Kalavrita on the 6 April (25 March according to the Julian calendar), but it is not at all clear that it ever actually occurred. By then it was scarcely necessary.

Meanwhile towards the end of March Isaias, the Bishop of Salona, had returned from Constantinople where he had discussed with the Patriarch Gregory and a number of Hetairists the uprising in Roumeli. Obviously the Bishop knew of 6 April as a possible date, but it was his view that Roumeli should only follow after the

Morea. On the evening of 24 March a meeting was held after vespers in the gallery of the church of Osios Loukas. Those present included Isaias, Diakos, Thanasis Zariphis (the Boeotian representative of the Hetairia), a number of the monks as well as leaders from Distomo, Arachova and other villages. Isaias told them of the imminence of the revolution and the need to make final preparations. Each person then took an oath on the Bible to work for a successful outcome.

The next day Isaias went to Salona to instruct the captains of Locris and Doris and the seamen of Galaxidi to make their preparations. Diakos returned to Levadia and meeting there with the three archons told them that he disagreed with Isaias; in view of Levadia's importance in Roumeli he thought it should revolt at the same time as the Morea and not after. Logothetis and Philonas agreed with him, but the elderly and cautious Nakos firmly held the opinion that the mountain areas should be first. The old man refused to change his mind and for several days the leaders of Levadia were at an impasse since Nakos was too widely respected for his opinion to be totally disregarded. Then a message came for Diakos to go to Patras to see the Hetairist Vlassopoulos. Plainly he would there be told of what was planned for the Morea and this might enable him to carry out his preferred design of a synchronised uprising throughout Roumeli.

Diakos himself was needed to stay close to Levadia, and in his place on 5 April he sent his protopallikar Vasilis Bousgos with two companions. They travelled to the Scala (the port) of Salona close to modern Itea and from there took a boat to Galaxidi. Once at Galaxidi Bousgos sought out the elders among the Galaxidiotes and asked them to arrange immediate transport for Patras. The reply he received was astonishing. 'You must be asleep at Levadia', one of the leaders informed him. 'Fighting began in the Morea days ago. You won't want to travel to Patras with a war on'. Bousgos' informant then pointed out to sea at some caiques which he said were bringing Turkish refugees from Vostitsa across the Gulf of Crisa to Scala. The news was indeed startling. It was now just 6 April — the earliest date envisaged for the uprising — and yet the Morea had risen several days before. All that remained for Bousgos to do was to travel back to Levadia and to inform Diakos before the news reached the ears of the Turkish governor; the Greeks must forestall any action by the Turks. Bousgos straightaway set off again. At Chriso he sent news of the uprising to Panourias, the captain of the armatolik at Salona, who was then at the nearby monastery of Prophitis Elias preparing to move against the Turks in Salona. At Arachova he gave instructions for the Greeks to hold the public roads to prevent the news of the Morea from travelling to Levadia.

It was late on the night of 6 April when the three men stopped to rest their exhausted horses at the (old) Khan of the Zemeno. They were there told that inside was sleeping a Turkish courier who was on his way from Salona to Levadia. Bousgos did not hesitate. He and his two men killed the Turk as well as his Albanian muleteer, and found on the courier letters informing the governor of Levadia about the events in the Morea. This killing at the Khan of Zemeno was the first blood spilt in Roumeli in the War of Independence.

When Vasilis arrived back at Levadia early the next morning, having covered in less than 48 hours a distance of some 160 kilometres, he went straight to his captain Diakos and gave him the letters captured at the Zemeno. The Roumeliot leader immediately sent for the three archons, but their meeting had barely begun when a message came that the governor, Hasan aga, wished to see them at once. Somehow the Turks had come to know of the murder and even to suspect the identity of the murderer. The Greek leaders had no choice but to go to Hasan at his office near the sources of the Hercyna and to deny any accusations made against Bousgos. Diakos was sent for as the responsible captain of armatoli, and he too heatedly denied his lieutenant's involvement in the murder. Bousgos had stayed the night at his house, he said. Finally the armatolos himself came into the room, and his demeanour — a compound of respect and indifference — at last persuaded Hasan that the Greeks were telling the truth. The capacity of the Greeks for such bold mendacity, a quality finely developed after centuries of dealing with the Turks, was only matched by the extraordinary naivety of the latter. If the story can be believed Diakos now displayed a quite brilliant touch. He had earlier promised that he would find the murderers, but as he rose to leave he suggested that the murder was the work of Odysseus who had returned to Roumeli with a large number of klephts and was threatening the ruin of the entire province.

Hasan was appalled. 'But cannot you gather an army from the vilaet to face Odysseus?' he asked.

'I can gather five to six thousand men' replied Diakos, 'but they need arms'. Arms were precisely what the Greeks needed most desperately. So great was the fear inspired in the aga by the prospect of Odysseus, and so great his trust in Diakos, that he immediately instructed his secretary to make out an order which he signed for the levying and arming of the Greeks. The Greeks could never have dared hope for so much.

The rest must be more briefly told. That evening Diakos after levying in the surrounding villages went to Osios Loukas where again he met Bishop Isaias. The next morning, 8 April, in the courtyard outside the church the cleric gave his blessing to the uprising and then exchanged his staff and mitre for a cutlass and pistol before travelling to the monastery of Prophitis Elias from which Panourias then set out to capture Salona. Diakos continued to collect men for his assault on the Turks at Levadia who had by now at last understood the nature of the events around them and had shut themselves up in the castle and clock tower and even in their own houses. In the early hours of 10 April Diakos left the monastery of Lycouresi near Chaironia, which had served as the meeting-place for his army, and marched against the garrison at Levadia. Hasan had prudently taken Logothetis and Nakos as hostages but was forced to exchange them for his own brother whom the monks of Osios Loukas had captured at Distomo. After clearing the houses of Turkish resistance, Diakos concentrated on the kastro and the clock tower. That night one section of the Greeks made repeated assaults against the castle up the steep slope above the gorge; another section poured fire into the first of the double walls to the north which was held by Moslem Albanian troops.

Neither attack was successful. The next day (12 April), in the words of the Greek historian of the revolution, Philemon, 'treachery succeeded where bravery had failed'. Logothetis entered into negotiations with the Albanians, and they deserted the Turks. Hasan aga, with his outer defences gone, then surrendered the kastro. The clock tower followed shortly afterwards. On 13 April — 1 April according to the old calendar — the flag of St George flew from the clock tower, and Diakos addressed a great crowd which had gathered in the area of the square which now bears his name. Diakos then went with the archons and other military leaders to attend a service of thanksgiving in the church of Ayia Paraskevi at which the three Bishops of Salona, Athens and Talanta all officiated. After the service Bishop Neophytos of Talanta officially gave Diakos the rank of colonel, and presenting him with a sword solemnly entrusted him with the duty of cutting off as many heads of the unfaithful as possible.

The War of Independence was a war between two religions, and being a holy war it resulted in acts of barbarism by Turk and Greek alike. After the fall of Levadia and Salona (which occurred on 22 April) most of the Turks — men, women and children — were killed despite all promises to the contrary. The same thing had also happened when the garrison towns of the Morea had surrendered.

In his poem *Hellas* dated 1 November 1821 Shelley correctly foresaw the ultimate triumph of the Greeks, though it happened after the poet's own death. Of the fall of the Turkish fortresses, which had already occurred, the poet wrote:

> the lust for blood,
> Which made our warriors drunk is quenched in death;
> But like a fiery plague breaks out anew
> In deeds which make the Christian cause look pale
> In its own light.

The Turks behaved no differently. I earlier spoke of the fate of Diakos and Bishop Isaias after the Greek reverse at Alamana. A little later Levadia itself suffered for its rebelliousness. In June of 1821 the Turks recaptured the city, slaughtered its inhabitants and burnt most of its buildings. The river Hercyna ran red.

I have not sought to exaggerate Levadia's importance in the early days of the war. As is well known the real centre of the outbreak was not here but in the Morea which too had its primates and kapoi (chiefs) such as Kolokotronis and which was also furthest from the reach of the Ottoman armies entering Greece from the north. For this same geographical reason, however, Roumeli bore the brunt of the Turkish attempts during the early years of the war to regain control, a situation aggravated by the installation of the new Greek government in the Peloponnese where the primates and chiefs and the new breed of politician remained more concerned with the advancement of their own positions than with the final defeat of the enemy. In this context, therefore, as one of the principal cities in Roumeli and with its fortress commanding the passes through Boeotia, Levadia was of more than local importance. Moreover the entire area of Levadia was a sufficient prize that Odysseus Androutsos was later prepared to act even against the Greek government itself in an attempt to retain its possession.

3

THE ORACLE OF TROPHONIUS

From the Plateia Diakou the Odhos Trophoniou runs beside the river towards the source of the stream. The direction is unmistakeable; there is a line of plane trees and an insistent rush of water. On either side the old factory buildings decay, all disused except for a single corn mill. The water falls over great steps, passes under bridges and drips from the side of the road. Ahead in the distance a great grey wall of rock appears — the further side of the gorge of the Hercyna. Near the tower that here descends from the Catalan castle, a fine Turkish bridge crosses the stream. The springs of the Hercyna are situated close to the bridge, but at this point one's attention is caught more by the gorge as it is now revealed running back into the mountains, a wild unimagined chaos of crags and boulders cast up and thrown down in defiance of the civilised world of streets and houses only a few minutes' walk away. Two small chapels alone have been built high up on the southern cliff — that of Ayios Minas and above it the chapel of the Source of Life (Zoodochos Pigi), a dependency of the monastery of Jerusalem at Davlia.

In its bed the gorge carries a winter torrent down from the upper regions of Mount Helicon. I have never walked up the gorge to its head, but there is this brief and romantic description in Frazer: '[The ravine's] deep, narrow stony bed, sometimes dry, sometimes traversed by a raging torrent, winds far into the heart of the mountains, shut in on either hand like a canyon by tremendous crags. If you follow it upwards for some miles, the country begins to open up and you find yourself in bleak and desolate highlands. A profound silence reigns, broken only by the cry of the water-ouzel beside the torrent or the screaming of hawks far up the cliffs.'†
Even in autumn I have not seen any water in the gorge and the perennial springs at its mouth must be unconnected with any winter torrent.

The springs themselves are obvious enough — one group emerges from the rocks to one side of the Xenia and another

†*Commentary on Pausanias*, Vol. 5, p. 197

beyond the bridge where a new pavement has been built on the opposite bank. In both areas there has been some interference with the natural flow of the sources, and with those near the Xenia in particular where some of the water has been ducted to flow in front of the Tourist Pavilion and the best of it has been channelled away altogether to form part of the town's water supply. Although there is no knowing the precise position of the springs there is little doubt that it was in this area that the waters of Forgetfulness and Memory drunk by an enquirer of the oracle of Trophonius were to be found. If additional evidence were necessary we have the statement of Gell that in the early nineteenth century one of the springs was yet known as Lephe, an obvious corruption of Lethe (Forgetfulness).

The river Hercyna itself was worshipped as a deity, and above the pavement mentioned earlier (over one of the springs) there are several niches in the rock which probably contained statues, among them images of the river, rather as at the Castalian Spring at Delphi. Two of the holes are much bigger. One is 4 metres square and 2.5 metres high with stone benches on either side which may have held reclining statues. In more recent times the Turkish governor whose office was nearby used to climb into the cave by wooden steps and here quietly smoke his pipe in the hottest part of the day. The other hole, below the first, has a rounder smaller

The Turkish bridge at the source of the river Hercyna, Levadia

entrance that goes back some 6 to 9 metres into the rock where there is said to be water. Its function remains uncertain.

The area as a whole by the springs is shown as Kria and it is hereabouts that one is directed to look for the famous oracle of Trophonius.

*

We might indeed have expected that the location of the oracle would have come to light by now since we have a detailed description of its structure in the pages of Pausanias, together with a more general picture of the relative layout of the major items of interest at Lebadea — including the oracle. Moreover Pausanias who was travelling in the second century AD had first-hand information, or so he says: 'What I write is not hearsay; I have myself inquired of Trophonius and seen other inquirers'. As we shall see, the description he gives of his descent to the oracle is graphic enough. However his more general topography remains characteristically vague when applied to the physical features of the area, and time has succeeded in effacing almost completely the remains of the buildings he mentions. The fact is that we do now know where the oracle was, and such inferences as we can make from the ancient writers including Pausanias suggest rather that the oracle was precisely not where we are now for convenience's sake directed to look for it, namely at the sources of the Hercyna.

Pausanias' description of his own consultation deserves quotation because it is perhaps the most remarkable description of its kind in ancient literature. The writer begins by telling us where the enquirer lodges before the consultation, and that 'among other regulations for purity he abstains from hot baths, bathing only in the river Hercyna'. Next we are told the gods to whom the enquirer sacrifices, including Apollo and Zeus, apart from Trophonius (who was little more than a local deity). Pausanias then continues as follows: 'The procedure of the descent is this. First, during the night he is taken to the river Hercyna by two boys...who after taking him there anoint him with oil and wash him...After this he is taken by the priests, not at once to the oracle, but to fountains of water very near to each other. Here he must drink water called the water of Forgetfulness, that he may forget all that he has been thinking of hitherto, and afterwards he drinks of another water, the water of Memory, which causes him to remember what he sees after his descent. After looking at the image which they say was made by Daedalus — it is not shown by the priests save to such as are going to visit Trophonius — having seen it, worshipped it and prayed, he proceeds to the oracle, dressed in a linen tunic, with ribbons girding it, and wearing the boots of the country. The oracle is on the mountain beyond the grove. Round it is a circular basement of white marble, the circumference of which is about that of the smallest threshing-floor, while its height is just short of two cubits [about a metre]. On the basement stand spikes, which like the cross-bars holding them together, are of bronze, while through them has been made a double door. Within the enclosure is a chasm in the earth, not natural, but artificially constructed after the most accurate masonry. The shape of this structure is like that of a bread oven. Its breadth across the middle one might conjecture to be about four cubits [2 metres], and its depth also could not be estimated to extend to more than cubits [4 metres]. They have made no way of descent to the bottom, but when a man comes to Trophonius they bring him a narrow, light ladder. After going down he finds a hole between the floor and the structure. Its breadth appeared to be two spans [about half a metre], and its height one span. The descender lies with his back on the ground, holding barley-cakes kneaded with honey, thrusts his feet into the hole and himself follows, trying hard to get his knees into the hole. After his knees the rest of his body is at once swiftly drawn in, just as the largest and most rapid river will catch a man in its eddy and carry him under. After this those who have entered the shrine learn the future, not in one and the same way in all cases, but by sight sometimes and at other times by hearing. The return upwards is by the same mouth, the feet darting out first. They say that no one who has made the descent has been killed save only one of the bodyguards of Demetrius. But they declare that he performed none of the usual rites in the sanctuary, and that he descended, not to consult the god but in the hope of stealing gold and silver from the shrine. It is said that the body of this man appeared in a different place, and was not cast out at the sacred mouth...After his ascent from Trophonius the enquirer is again taken in hand by the priests, who set him upon a chair called the chair of Memory, which stands not far from the shrine, and they ask of him, when seated there, all he has seen or learnt. After gaining this information they then entrust him to his relatives. These lift him, paralysed with terror and unconscious both of himself and of his surroundings, and carry him to the building where he lodged before...Afterwards, however, he will recover all his faculties, and the power to laugh will return to him...Those who have descended into the shrine of Trophonius are obliged to dedicate a tablet on which is written all that each has heard or seen.'†

Pausanias does not however give us any detail of the nature of what he himself saw or heard, but the entire experience was obviously very frightening — sufficiently so that the inability to laugh was said sometimes to be permanent. There was even a proverb used of a gloomy and dark-looking person, 'He has been at the oracle of Trophonius'. Sometimes the enquirer did not recover from his visit. Plutarch, a native of nearby Chaironia, tells the story of the descent of a man called Timarchus. Once inside the oracular crypt Timarchus was said to have been struck on the head before seeing a vision about the nature of the soul, after which he felt another sharp pain in his head and lost consciousness altogether. He eventually came to his senses in the same spot where he had first laid down. The poor man had been underground for two days and a night. Three months later he died.

Despite scepticism on the part of some, the oracle of Trophonius alone of the Boeotian oracles survived until the time of Plutarch and later. Its survival must have been partly due to its fame in more remote periods of history. King Croesus had sent to Trophonius when he was testing the accuracy of the Greek oracles, and Mardonius the Persian general also consulted the oracle in the winter of 480/479 BC, as did the general Sulla at the time of the battle of Chaironia — although none of these three made a personal visit. Possibly a more significant aspect of the oracle at Lebadea was its connection with Delphi. There are several points at which Delphi enters into the myth of Trophonius. According to one tradition the birth of Trophonius (to King Erginus of Orchomenos) was in fulfilment of a Pythian oracle. Later Trophonius and his brother Agamedes were said to have been the architects of the first stone temple at Delphi. Then after the earth had swallowed up Trophonius at Lebadea it was the Pythian priestess who revealed to the Boeotians the existence of his oracle.

†Description of Greece, Book IX, 39.7. Translated by WHS Jones (Loeb edition). This work of Pausanias, written in Greek, remains an invaluable record of the monuments, legends, history, etc, of the places he visited on his travels. Frequent reference is made to it in later pages.

It is possible too that those travelling to consult the Pythia may sometimes have first visited the oracle of Trophonius in the hope that the two answers would coincide, as happened in the *Ion* of Euripides. The two procedures were quite different, with the priestess giving the god's answer at Delphi, whereas at Lebadea the enquirer saw the future himself 'by sight or hearing' without any intermediary. Collusion between the two oracles therefore seems unlikely, although a tradition remains at Levadia that formerly a tunnel led from one place to the other.

Whatever be the explanation — its association with Delphi or the unusual nature of the experience involved in the consultation — the oracle at Lebadea somehow outlasted the other Boeotian centres, and yet has disappeared as surely as if it had never existed.

*

Various suggestions have been made as to the position of the oracle. It has been placed as far apart as at the chapels of Ayia Varvara (in the kastro) and Zoodochos Pigi (in the gorge), neither of which can be correct. However, even if we cannot be sure exactly where it was, we can get some general idea by looking for the other principal features mentioned by Pausanias at Lebadea, in particular the site of the ancient city itself as well as of the grove of Trophonius and the temple of Zeus.

When Pausanias visited the oracle in the second half of the second century AD he said of Lebadea that 'the city is no less adorned than the most prosperous of the Greek cities'. Yet so completely had any traces of Lebadea disappeared from view that it became until very recently a matter of some speculation where exactly the ancient city had been. Some even put it at the hill of Tripolithari, better known today under the name of the church of Ayios Vlasios, which is on the northern edge of the modern town beside the road towards Chaironia; here some ancient foundations and tombs have been found. However after the excavations carried out by Ioannis Threpsiades in 1956 in the Odhos Christodoulou (near the Plateia of George I), when he discovered the remains of some large walls belonging to an important building of the end of the fourth or beginning of the third century BC and concluded that these walls (which he suggested may have belonged to a temple of Cybele) formed part of the agora or market-place of the ancient city, there can be little doubt that Lebadea occupied some part of the area presently taken up by the modern town. As the traveller goes on to say that 'the city is separated from the grove of Trophonius by the river Hercyna', we can fairly conclude that the city principally occupied the east bank of the Hercyna (for it is on that side that the remains of the agora have come to light) and that the grove of Trophonius was therefore on the west bank.

We would expect the grove to be near the water of the Hercyna, and Pliny in his *Natural History* says as much. There is no reason to suppose that the river took a very different course from today, and one obvious possibility for the site of the grove of Trophonius containing his temple would be in the vicinity of the church of the Panagia in Plateia Diakou. It was here that Spon and Wheler found, in the yard of the mosque that preceded the church, two inscriptions which apart from confirming the identity of Levadia with Lebadea spoke of dedications to Trophonius. Although other inscriptions have been found at other points in the city which also refer to Trophonius, the area of the plateia certainly fits what we can gather from the ancient writers.

Then there is the oracle itself. With the position of the grove and temple of Trophonius tentatively established, we can get some idea of the approximate whereabouts of the oracle from some further evidence Pausanias gives us. For our ancient traveller says two things about it — he describes the oracle as being 'on the mountain beyond the grove', and at another point he says, 'if you go up to the oracle and thence onwards up the mountain you come to...the temple of Zeus'. Now we know where the temple of Zeus was situated, because the remains of the building which was never completed can be seen on the very top of Ayios Elias.

On one recent visit to Levadia I heard several people declare that the oracle had at last been found on the summit of the hill, and so I set out with some anticipation to walk up to the temple. Though you can reach the upper part of Ayios Elias from other areas of the town, it is perfectly easy to proceed from the site of the imaginary grove in the area of the Plateia Diakou, past the kastro and in about twenty to thirty minutes from the kastro reach the temple. It is worth the walk. Above the kastro there is a wide stretch of grass, soft with water, a meadow that runs between two lines of small houses sitting like English bungalows on the edge of the sands. From this point you obtain a particularly good idea of the kastro as it rises in three tiers, almost complete, to the ruined tower and the church at its highest point — much as it appeared in the days of the

Catalans, only today it is green with vegetation. To the left the grey walls of the gorge twist their way up into the hills. At the top of this rise you encounter a dirt road that goes from the upper level of the town over a ridge to the village of Analipsis. The summit of Ayios Elias lies across a small valley to the right, and having followed the road you must take a right-hand fork along a ridge which connects with the top of the hill.

Once on the hilltop you immediately realise that Ayios Elias is at the centre of the surrounding heights, with Helicon on the south and the Thourion range over towards Chaironia on the north. It was a natural site for a temple, and the Lebadeans evidently dissatisfied with the more modest temple still to be seen in the second century AD had started to build a large new temple to Zeus. However they never finished the building, according to Pausanias 'either because of its size or because of the long succession of the wars'. At the time of my visit the recent excavations had laid bare the foundations of the temple of Zeus about half a metre below the stony surface, but there was still no sign of the oracle — that was mere rumour.

Nor, to return to Pausanias, would you expect the oracle of Trophonius to be so close to the temple of Zeus as to be actually on the summit of the hill. It is clear that the enquirer could proceed from the grove of Trophonius up the hill to the oracle and thence onwards to the temple of Zeus, and that therefore the oracle lay somewhere between these two points, although not necessarily in a direct line. The only detail we can add to this picture, a statement from Philostratus that the oracle lay 'a little above the temple [of Trophonius]' suggests it was on the lower slopes of Ayios Elias or the kastro hill itself rather than higher up. Moreover the distance otherwise involved for the priests and enquirers to walk from the purifying waters of the Hercyna similarly points to a relatively low position for the oracle.

If we disregard the pit under the floor of Ayia Varvara at the top of the kastro which turned out to have been a cistern, it seems at first surprising that no chasm or cave of a suitable kind has come to light in an area so close to the town during the last few centuries of enquiry by numerous antiquaries. Almost certainly any natural cave would have been found by now, even under the inhabited area. Yet Pausanias makes it clear that the structure which he compared with a bread oven was completely artificial, being 'built in the most careful manner'. Also Philostratus speaks of it being in, or on, a hill of earth, and he uses a Greek word that could well mean an artificial mound. Does not then the probable reason why we cannot find the oracle become plain? Both the masonry and the mound in which it was situated, the entire structure made by man, could have disappeared as surely as the temple of Trophonius, crumbling away in the passage of time or even deliberately destroyed by the early Christians, without leaving any noticeable trace on the ground whatsoever. No doubt the quest for Trophonius will continue, but his hole in the ground has gone.

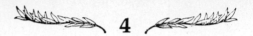

4

TO CHAIRONIA

For a long time the principal road from Levadia to Delphi did not follow the modern route westwards via Tsoukalades and across the outlying hills of Helicon but chose the more level way through Chaironia, Ayios Vlasios (Panopeos) and the territory of Davlia to the valley of Keresi and the area of the Schist Road. This was so in the ancient period, and indeed up to the present century the more direct route westwards from Levadia was little more than a track. The motor road via Tsoukalades was only built in 1931, and it remained a difficult route until recently realigned.

It is the old road to Delphi — the Sacred Way — that we shall follow, and fortunately soon after leaving Levadia the way diverges from the motor traffic on the main road to the north and instead passes directly over Mount Thourion to Chaironia via the Kerata pass. At last, if you are going to walk to Chaironia, you can strap on some strong boots or shoes, pick up a flask of water (a general principle, though in this case the journey takes less than two hours) and set off with that great sense of freedom that comes from travelling on foot.

However, to begin with, you have to walk out of Levadia for a quarter of an hour or so along the main road to Brallos and Lamia (and incidentally the road from which you turn right after some 5 kilometres to go to Orchomenos). You pass the church and hill of Ayios Vlasios, cross the Hercyna stream and continue a short way until the road turns sharply to the right to pass round Mount Thourion. At this point a dirt road leads off to the left by a white marble shrine with a poignant inscription recording the final visit of a Levadite to his hometown in 1975 after an absence of sixty-five years — 'I shall not return again to see Levadia', he says. The dirt track follows the line of the old road, and leads past a skinning factory guarded by some ferocious dogs and on up the side of the hill.

The ferocity of Greek dogs, particularly in country areas where they may be guarding animals, is a well-worn theme among the early travellers and to this day it is quite common to be warned against doing a particular walk because of the dogs — 'they'll eat

you', you are told. And it is true that some of the shepherd dogs are
very large and appear to be very aggressive. However, the remedy
is usually to hand in the form of the large stones that will probably
be littering the path that you are treading and which often provided
ammunition for the Homeric heroes in battle. As a rule nothing
more is necessary to prevent attack than to make as if to pick up a
stone since centuries of maltreatment have bred into the Greek
animal the instinct to turn tail at this point. One visitor in the
seventeenth century even noticed that dogs were not to be seen in
a Greek church (implying that elsewhere in Europe they were)
owing he thought to the terror inspired by the frequent bowing of
the congregation which the animal used to mistake for the act of
lifting a stone. It is seldom that you ever need to throw the weapon.
There is also said to be one last desperate act if all else fails, and that
is to do what Odysseus did when he was attacked by Eumaeus'
dogs as he approached his farm, and sit down on the ground. I
would rather not try it.

Once safely past the dogs, the track soon arrives at a plateau on
the top of the low hills, and here there is a delightful walk of half an
hour or so across a green sward to the Kerata pass on the further
side. At some points it is possible to see signs of the former stone-
paved road under the grass, and for some distance the kerb can be
detected along one side of it. Then where the ground begins to fall,
just above the defile down to the plain of Chaironia, there is a short
stretch of some 50 to 100 metres of paved road in an almost perfect
state of preservation, stepped in places to assist the passage of the
mules and horses that would have formed most of the traffic.

Stretches of cobbled road like this do not date from antiquity.
They are known today by the name kaldirimi, a Turkish word, and
are in fact remnants of the highways built by the Turks. Until the
period of the Turkish occupation the roads in Greece were mostly
little more than tracks following the shortest route possible,
sometimes even along riverbeds; few routes were intended for
wheeled traffic, and such as were simply had wheel-ruts cut into
them where the ground was particularly uneven. The majority of
travellers in antiquity (and later) rode or walked, and despite the
new roads most Turks must have done the same, only the
wealthiest being carried by litter between mules and the most
powerful like the pashas being bumped along in carriages. The
European travellers usually hired horses or mules from an
agogiates (muleteer) who would then act as a local guide — a

Centenarian Sarakatsanos at Chaironia

system of travel that has stopped only quite recently.

Shortly after this stretch of kaldirimi the way enters a small defile down to the plain. It is this part of the road that it is now known as Ta Kerata, The Horns. The reason for this name I began to understand as I started to descend the path on the right hand side of the narrow valley. There on the ground lay a number of curiously shaped pieces of stone. Curling and slightly fluted the stones looked exactly like parts of petrified goats' horns. Those I saw were only a few centimetres long but it was obvious that they had belonged to larger pieces before being broken. I did not at first know what they were.

At the bottom of the Kerata pass there is a dirt road which if followed northwestwards leads after about half an hour to the village of Chaironia. One day as I came this way I encountered a hospitable family that lives in one of the modest single storey houses that stand on the edge of this side of the village. At first there was a young man, dark, with fine hard-chiselled features. Standing in the sun he asked from where I had come, and I indicated the hills behind us. 'Apo ta Kerata', he said. I learnt he was a student of law at Thessaloniki University and that he was home on holiday. As we talked an old man came out of the house. He was very short and was bent over a shepherd's crook. His face was wrinkled like the shell of a walnut. On his head there was a small brimless lambskin cap. He walked slowly over to a wooden crate and sat down on it holding the crook in front of him and watching us with alert eyes. The young man then told me that this was his grandfather and, in the matter of fact way the Greeks have in talking of the old in their presence, said he was over a hundred years old. By now two women each of an age to be the old man's daughters had come out into the October sun, and Ioannis (for this was the young man's name) told me with some pride that they were all Sarakatsani. He pointed out the kalpaki (the cap) on his grandfather's head, which is the traditional headgear of the Sarakatsanos shepherd.

At this time I knew of the Sarakatsani settled at the next village of Thourion. I did not yet know of any at Chaironia. I turned to the old shepherd and asked him where he had been born.

'In Karpenisi', he replied. 'Years ago we came down here and lived for a long time in kalives (huts) at Kerata. Then fifteen years ago we moved to this house', and the Sarakatsanos lifted his crook to point towards the rudely-built brick building behind him, suggesting by his manner the quiet acceptance of a form of shelter both more comfortable and less dignified than the traditional kind in which he had spent most of his life.

I too was now seated and was being pressed by one of the women to accept a small glass of vermouth together with a delicious gliko (sweet) made from quince. The woman moved away leaving the tray beside me and occupied herself with her loom which despite the advancing autumn still stood outside the house with chickens scratching around its base. I asked then about the horn-like pieces of stone, and Ioannis told me the story of the Kerata.

'One time', he said, 'there was a shepherd with a great many goats. He had some five hundred animals or more. But he was never satisfied and he was mean too. One day when he was with his goats over there in the defile, a stranger came to him and asked for some cheese as he was hungry. The shepherd had plenty of cheese but offered the stranger only a tiny amount', and here Ioannis indicated the tip of his finger, 'and nothing more. The next day the stranger came to him and again asked for some cheese. The shepherd gave him a similar amount as before. Now the stranger it turned out was no ordinary person but was in truth Jesus Christ. And Christ was angry with the shepherd's meanness. So he straightaway turned the shepherd's cheese into stone and he did the same to every one of his animals. You can see what became of the cheese. On the right of the path as you begin to ascend the pass there is a large stone known as To Turi (The Cheese).' I dimly remembered a round rock, slightly split at one end. 'And you can still see the horns of the goats in the stones on the ground as you get towards the top. There aren't as many as there were once', Ioannis went on, 'the animals have broken the stones as they have passed and people have picked them up and scattered them to one side. I am surprised you even noticed them.'

Ioannis had spoken as if he believed every word of the story, though without doubt the tale and its telling counted for more with him than its truth. The truth is simple enough. The horn-like pieces of stone are in reality fossils from a large species of shellfish of the mollusc family that was about a third of a metre long and was a contemporary of the dinosaurs. Though their shells could vary greatly, some long and thin, others thick and curling, they have in their fossilised state a remarkable similarity to goats' horns. And thus they have given rise to the myth of Ta Kerata.

I mentioned earlier the Sarakatsani at the nearby village of Thourion. This is situated on the main road between Levadia and Chaironia, and I had visited it a few days previously. I had been wandering over the battlefield of Chaironia looking for the burial mound of the Macedonian dead. The mound lies out in the plain, a little nearer to Thourion than to the village of Chaironia, and I had later walked across the fields to Thourion with the idea of looking at the reed huts on the hillside behind the village. I then believed, wrongly, that the huts belonged to Vlachs.

As often happens I fetched up initially at the kafeneion. It was mid-morning, and at one of the tables in the small room which was bereft of any ornament except a cracked mirror on one wall there sat a group of men who as I came in were calling for another kilo of retsina. There was a fat round-faced man in the dishevelled uniform of an agrophilakas (field-guard), and the local postman called Nikos whom I knew from Davlia. The group was completed by two older men, one of whom was already starting to break into snatches of song. The fourth man was less ebullient, and he possessed unusual features; his nose was long and was pressed back against his face, and his skin reddened by the sun and wind was stretched tightly across flat cheekbones.

Nikos called me over to keep company with them, and in return I was bound to satisfy their curiosity. Where had I been, I was asked, and the agrophilakas nodded sagely when I spoke of the mound. But why had I come to Thourion? I suggested it was because of the wine, and so the two older men pleased with this thought launched into a drinking song. By stretching the syllables into an infinity of garbled modulations they spent some time singing these few lines:

> If the drunkards are condemned
> Wrongly they'll be hanged;
> I am no drunkard
> But I like a drop
> Because of two blue eyes.
> Why, oh why do you threaten
> That somewhere else you'll go —
> Go on then, go.

The maudlin sentiment was in keeping with the long, drawn-out tones of the singers as they leant back and raised their half-closed eyes towards the ceiling in rigid concentration, their heads shaking slightly as each sound, once savoured and swilled around the mouth like a gulp of wine, was forced out to give way to the next. When at last they had finished they called for more wine and once refreshed continued with a klephtic song.

In the next interval I took the opportunity to ask about the Vlachs at Thourion. Nikos, whose morning delivery of post was going to be completed in the afternoon if at all, was quick to point out that they were not Vlachs at all but Sarakatsani, and it became clear that one of the older men at the table, the man with the flat features, was a Sarakatsanos. He was about sixty and said he had been in Thourion for some fifty years. According to him there were about fifteen Sarakatsani families here, and in every case the head of the family was a shepherd. At one time they had all lived in huts made of reeds such as I had seen on the hillside behind the village, but now they all had their own houses. I enquired about the grazing of their animals, whether they travelled far for summer pasture, as both Sarakatsani and Vlachs have traditionally done. I learnt that the previous summer only one shepherd had gone elsewhere for grazing, the rest had kept their herds either on the plain in rented fields or on the communal land on the hills nearby.

Traditional shelter of the nomadic Sarakatsani at Thourion

All this conversation was without obvious emotion, but then a look of sadness passed over the face of the Sarakatsanos. 'The trouble now', he said, 'is that the children are leaving the profession. I have three children and not one is a shepherd.' His sadness was deeper than that of the shepherds of many another village who of course say the same, that the young men will not continue the work because the life is hard and the return small. In his case he knew what this meant for the traditional way of life of the Sarakatsani, already much changed by the move away from nomadism to conventional settlement.

I left the convivial party in the kafeneion and walked onto the hill to the south of the village where there are several of the Sarakatsani dwellings of not many years ago. The huts are basically made of reed which is laid vertically and then secured horizontally by long pieces of bamboo. One hut was completely circular like the shape of an igloo, but most were rectangular with pitched roofs of the same material. Outside these huts, enclosures had been built for the animals made of a loose wattle and lined with bundles of reed to provide shelter from the wind. It was not difficult to imagine such an encampment with the shepherds and their families quartered next to the animals in the enclosures. At Thourion at any rate that time has passed. The huts are now madri (shelters) for the animals and their young, and there was not a single human inhabitant to be seen.

*

It is a fairly common mistake to refer to the Sarakatsani as Vlachs, and I had been misled by local people into doing just that at Thourion. Sometimes the word Vlach is used of any Greek shepherd, but apart from that general use it properly refers to a quite distinct group within Greece, more particularly known as the Koutsovlachs, who despite some superficial similarities in their way of life are to be distinguished from the Sarakatsani. The most important difference, though one which is fast disappearing, is that the Sarakatsani are by tradition true nomads, in that they would have had no permanent settlement as they moved with their animals from one pasture to the next. The Vlachs on the other hand have been semi-nomadic; they have as a rule possessed permanent homes in the mountains, particularly the Pindos, from which they would move in the autumn to pasture their flocks in the plain and to which they have returned in the spring. Increasingly the Vlachs have created villages in place of their more rudimentary winter quarters, but the element of travel between summer and winter pasture has often remained.

Another distinction between the two groups is that of language. The Sarakatsani speak Greek, whereas the first language of the Vlachs is of Latin origin and closely akin to Roumanian. It is not clear from where either group derives. Possibly the Vlachs were originally the Latinised local inhabitants of Roman provinces to the north of Greece, of Thrace and Moesia to the south of the Danube or even of Dacia (modern Roumania) on the far side; at some point they were driven south into the mountain areas and there took up or continued their shepherding. In the twelfth century the Vlachs had become sufficiently concentrated in the region of Thessaly that they formed the virtually independent state of Great Wallachia, and it is still in the Pindos area that they are mostly to be found today. On the other hand the fact that the Sarakatsani speak Greek and that some of their customs retain pagan elements such as the mock wedding on the first day of Lent has encouraged the view that this proud race who seldom marry outside their own people may derive directly from some section of the inhabitants of ancient Greece. If that is so, the ancestors of the Sarakatsani were as far removed in physical type from at least those ancient Greeks that we see portrayed in sculpture, albeit the portraits were often idealised, as they remain distinctive today.

*

Pausanias proceeded from Lebadea to Chaironia, almost certainly by the Kerata pass, and he describes arriving at the city in this matter: 'As you approach the city you see a common grave of the Thebans who were killed in the struggle against Philip. It has no inscription, but is surmounted by a lion, probably a reference to the spirit of the men'.† The same lion, faithfully restored, still greets the visitor whether he is arriving on foot or travelling along the main road. The monument is certainly arresting. The attitude of the lion as he sits up on his haunches, his ribs showing below the massive shoulders and his forelegs stretched out ramrod straight, is that of complete alertness. The mouth is drawn back slightly and

†Book IX, 40.10, translated by W H S Jones

the teeth bared as if he is about to let out a low roar. He guards a tomb, but as Pausanias observed he also breathes something of the spirit of the men who had fought and died in the great battle that took place in the fields nearby. Not everyone shares the view of Pausanias that the lion is guarding the Theban dead — at least one scholar has suggested it was rather the burial place of the

The lion at Chaironia

Macedonians under Philip who fell on the right wing — but the expression of proud defiance befits better the vanquished than the victors.

Originally the lion stood above a mound. At the beginning of the last century only fragments could be seen, half-buried in the earth, and local people believing it to be the remains of a statue of a boar (kapros) had called the village Kapraina. In 1818 some visiting Englishmen identified the statue as that of the lion mentioned by Pausanias but it was further damaged during the War of Independence by Odysseus Androutsos who thought it might contain treasure. The rest of the animal was found in 1879 during the excavation of the tomb, when beneath the mound 254 skeletons were discovered, crammed together like sardines, within a rectangular stonework enclosure. Finally in 1904 the lion was restored and re-erected on top of the original plinth.

If you wish to envisage the area of the battlefield and in particular where the Thebans fell, you might follow the lion's gaze across the innocent-looking fields of cotton and corn towards the other side of the plain where the Cephisos ambles peacefully along. The battle lines of the two armies stretched between the river and the city of Chaironia as the Greek army attempted in the summer of 338 BC to prevent the Macedonians advancing down the valley of the Cephisos into central Greece. Even if the topographical detail of the battle is not altogether certain, we do know the position of the extreme right wing of the Greek army. This consisted of the elite corps of the Theban army, the sacred band of about three hundred men, and it was posted on the near bank of the Cephisos. During the battle the sacred band was destroyed by Philip's son, Alexander, and in his *Life of Alexander* Plutarch adds another detail indicating its position: 'At the battle of Chaeronea which his father fought against the Grecians, he is said to have been the first man that charged the Thebans' sacred band. And even in my remembrance there stood an old oak tree near the river Cephisus, which people called Alexander's oak, because his tent was pitched under it. And not far off are to be seen the graves of the Macedonians who fell in that battle.'† There is now no oak tree, but the Macedonian burial mound remains and we can reasonably assume that it stands close to the place where the Macedonians fell in the savage fighting with the Thebans, who we are told stood

†*Alexander* IX, 2–3, translated by Dryden

their ground until they were nearly all killed. The Greek right wing was therefore positioned close to the burial place of the Macedonians.

The Macedonian mound is located not far from the river, about 3 kilometres east of Chaironia village and due south of the village of Akontion; it lies close to the south side of the railway line and is about twenty minutes or so walk from the railway station. The mound is newly planted with cypresses, and bamboo grows in the hollow centre which Sotiriades excavated at the beginning of the century. The mound was dated to the fourth century BC and contained on the level of the plain the thick ashes of a huge funeral pyre, mixed with bones and half-charred pieces of wood. In addition to some fourth century vases and Macedonian coins, Sotiriades found the lance-heads of some Macedonian sarissas now in Chaironia Museum, making identification complete.

The Greek line thus stretched from near this point back across the plain to the edge of the ancient city, which like the modern village occupied mainly the mouth of the small valley below and to the east of the acropolis. Indeed the left wing of the Greek army comprising the Athenians would have rested close to the eventual position of the lion monument. The strategy of the Greek position was not only to deny Philip's advance but also to retain a line of retreat over the Kerata pass to Lebadea. In the event the strategy was wise, since after their defeat most of the Greek army must have made its escape that way, including the Athenian architect of Greek resistance to Philip, the orator Demosthenes, who threw down his shield and ran with the best.

*

It is common to speak of the battle of Chaironia as if it spelt the end of freedom for the Greeks.

'That dishonest victory
At Chaironea fatal to liberty',

Milton wrote. Certainly it was the victory of an absolute monarch over the independent and often democratic cities of Greece. But its significance lay more in the fact that for the first time the supremacy obtained on the battlefield was not that of one of the Greek cities over others as in the past but of a new nation from outside old Greece over the traditional centres of power. The long period of importance of the city-states was over, and they became little more than the guardians of Hellenic culture within the more diverse and far-flung worlds of the Macedonian and then the Roman empires. That fate was probably inevitable as long as the cities remained as competitive and jealous of position as historically they had been, and it was precisely their rivalries and divisions that had led to the intervention of Philip of Macedon. It was oddly appropriate that Delphi, where the rivalries and victories of one city over another had been frequently celebrated in its elaborate treasuries and dedications, should have provided the central scene for the final acts in this most enduring Greek tragedy.

Following the brief period of Theban supremacy after the battle of Leuctra in 371 BC, the Phocians† once again asserted their independence from the Boeotian League of which Thebes was the leader, only to find themselves the target of Theban malice within the politics of the body controlling Delphi, the Amphictyonic Council. When on a pretext some of the Phocian leaders were fined for sacrilege they reacted by seizing Delphi itself under their general Philomelos of Ledon. In the long war that ensued against the Boeotians (who were supported by the Locrians, the Thessalians and also by Philip of Macedon), the Phocians who had only limited assistance from the Athenians and Spartans nonetheless succeeded in establishing themselves in control of much of central Greece, although in doing so they were forced to make use of the treasures of Delphi to pay for mercenaries. Finally in 346 BC Philip at the invitation of Thebes and the Thessalians entered central Greece and crushed the Phocians who by this time were quarelling among themselves. The Amphictyonic Council voted that the Phocian cities be destroyed (which in practice must have meant that their walls were pulled down) and the inhabitants moved away to villages. The Phocians were further deprived of any participation in the Delphic sanctuary and their position on the

†Nowadays the county or nome of Phocis lies along the north coast of the Gulf of Corinth, from Delphi in the east almost as far as Navpactos in the west; its capital is Amphissa and the nome stretches inland to include the mountains of Giona. But this is almost entirely to the west of ancient Phocis. In antiquity Phocis lay principally on the east and south of Parnassos, although Delphi could also be claimed as a Phocian city. The boundary of Phocis with the Boeotians then lay just to the west of Lebadea and north of Chaironia, whereas today Boeotia includes the summits of Parnassos and even Arachova. West of ancient Phocis were the Ozolian Locrians, and Amphissa was then a Locrian city. In fact today Phocis more or less occupies the former territory of the Locrians.

Council was taken by the Macedonians, who thus established a permanent voice in Greek affairs.

Theban moves within the Amphictyonic Council, this time against Athens, provide also the background to Philip's final triumph at Chaironia, though at the critical moment the Thebans ended by siding with the Athenians. In the years after the end of the Phocian war the Athenians under the misguided influence of Demosthenes followed an increasingly hostile policy towards Macedon. The occasion for open hostilities only arose in the following way. During the time of Phocian control over Delphi in the earlier sacred war, their Athenian allies had pointedly rededicated the donation of gold shields first set up by them after the victory at Plataia over the Persians and their Theban allies. At the instigation of Thebes the Amphissans proposed to the Amphictyonic Council that the Athenians be fined for an act of sacrilege, since the rededication occurred when Delphi was in the hands of the Phocians who had stolen many of its treasures. The Athenians cleverly countered by charging the Amphissans with the greater infamy of cultivating the sacred plain below Delphi which centuries before had been dedicated to Apollo and was normally only used for the pasture of animals. The Amphictyons were persuaded to march down into the fields to destroy the crops, but they were then attacked by the Amphissans and forced to withdraw. The Amphictyonic Council, by now diverted from action against Athens, was unable to enforce its decrees against the Amphissans; the Thebans would not lend assistance against their ally, and even the Athenians would do nothing since Demosthenes was already working for a common allegiance against Philip and he feared further entanglement with Thebes.

Thus once again Philip was invited, this time by the Amphictyonic Council to take the lead in a sacred war. In the spring of 338 BC the Macedonians quickly advanced through the pass of Thermopylae and crossed Kallidromon to seize the Phocian city of Elatia, thereby controlling the principal route through Phocis into central Greece. Another force was sent to occupy the mountain pass between Doris and Amphissa. The Locrian city was only the pretext for Philip's advance — the time had come for the decisive struggle with Athens. Here the position of Thebes, astride Philip's route into Attica, could prove critical. Ambassadors from both the Athenians and the Macedonians went before the assembly at Thebes to argue their respective cases for an alliance. The vote was won for Athens, in good measure by the rhetoric of Demosthenes but also because even the selfish Thebans appreciated that with Athens defeated they too would be the servants of Philip. Demosthenes now succeeded in drumming together a confederate Greek army comprising not only the Thebans and Athenians but also the Phocians and various states from the Peloponnese. This force took up a position in the pass of Parapotamii near Elatia defending the route along the Cephisos. When however in the summer a Macedonian detachment advanced and captured Amphissa, the Greeks were forced to fall back to Chaironia. Here they could guard both the route from the north and also that to the west from Amphissa and the Schist Road.

The outcome of the battle that followed was a total victory for Philip, who to add to his satisfaction took a large number of Athenian prisoners. Yet there was no pursuit of those that fled, and it is likely that this was due to political considerations. In almost every respect the Macedonian monarch showed great magnaminity. He did not repeat on the Greeks the harsh punishment meted out to the Phocians after the previous sacred war. On the contrary Philip was almost certainly responsible for a whole new generation of walling in both Phocis and elsewhere.† He did not march on Athens and seek to humble his implacable enemy, as well he might have done. The only city to suffer was Thebes, where Philip after killing some of his political opponents and dismantling the Boeotian League imposed a Macedonian garrison. (The destruction of the city by Alexander was not until two years later when the Thebans had attempted to eject the Macedonian garrison). The king must even have disregarded the grandiose monument which the Thebans raised at Chaironia over their dead

†The walling of many Phocian cities is of a remarkably uniform style, classified as a form of 'isodomic trapezoidal' by R L Scrutton, *Greek Walls* (1941). An example may be seen in the photograph on page 122 of part of a fine tower from the enclosure at Tithorea. These walls must date from after 346 BC when we know the Phocian cities were destroyed following the Phocian War. The same style is found at Amphissa which had been destroyed just before Chaironia, and at Plataia which according to Pausanias was restored by Philip after the battle. The overwhelming probability is that restoration of all these cities and indeed the fortification in this style of the other Locrian cities apart from Amphissa — such as those at Galaxidi and Ayia Evthymia — went ahead in the same period after the battle of Chaironia and could only have occurred with the consent, even encouragement, of the Macedonians.

heroes. Indeed the actions of Philip after Chaironia reveal a rare gift of statesmanship. He appreciated that it was a far more import- ant task to win the free acknowledgement of Macedonian leader- ship from the old centres of power in Greece than merely to main- tain military domination over them. In this respect his policy was only partially successful. The appointment of Philip by a later con- gress of Greek cities at Corinth as the commander of a pan-Hellenic army against Persia cost the Greeks little since they made no great contribution to the eventual expedition. On the other hand when after Philip's assassination at Pella Alexander took over his father's command he was able to march against the East, nominally at any rate, as the leader of all Greece.

*

The most famous citizen of Chaironia remains Plutarch, the moralist and the author of the *Parallel Lives*. Plutarch spent much of his life at Chaironia, where he was born in about AD 46. He had studied at Athens and had travelled widely both within Greece and abroad; he had gone to Rome where he lectured on ethical subjects and also to Alexandria and Asia Minor. However despite belonging to the wider world of the early Roman empire, he was in the tradition of Greek philosophy and scholarship, and he chose to live in the small provincial city of Chaironia where he continued to lecture and to write. As a stout upholder of the values of the old religion and philosophies, Plutarch even became at one time a priest at Delphi.

In his *Life of Demosthenes*, when referring to the advantages to a historian of living in a large town with plenty of books and also with access to other people's memories, Plutarch wittily expresses his preference for living in Chaironia — 'But for me I live in a small town, where I am willing to continue lest it grow less'. In fact there was little danger of the city becoming depopulated. By that time Greece had become a Roman province and the cities, which still enjoyed considerable local freedom of government within their traditional territories, were protected under the Pax Romana from their most destructive rivalries. Chaironia itself, with the advantage of the fertile plain in front of it and also the pasture land behind, was now prospering further from a profitable industry that manufactured unguents from flowers such as the lily, the rose, narcissus and iris. If the town could no longer be compared to a

Landscape behind Chaironia

city-state of the fifth century it was certainly no mere country retreat. It retained the usual public buildings, and Plutarch himself was at one time an archon or magistrate.

The acropolis of Chaironia stood on the rocky outcrop known then as Petrachos which may be seen directly above the theatre. The city itself lay chiefly to the east and south of the acropolis along the valley that runs beneath it. The walls of the enceinte which can still be traced around most of the circuit embraced two small peaks separated by a saddle. The wall on the east has almost entirely disappeared owing to its proximity to the surviving village; in some places it is just possible to make out its line where the lowest level of rocks on the slope have been hewn to take the base of the wall. It was on this side that entrance to the acropolis was gained and it is also the easiest approach to the acropolis today (you must first walk through the village). On the other sides the walls survive at points up to ten courses high. On the north side (towards the plain) the wall can be made out along almost the entire length where it was built on top of the rocks. To the south there are the remains of three towers. On the west of the circuit there is one most unusual feature; in one section the wall has been deliberately raked back at an angle, although it is difficult to see what advantage this could give to the defenders.† All the walls are built of the grey rock of the hill itself and are of the same style noticed earlier in connection with Philip's restoration of the Greek cities after the battle in 338.

The ancient theatre lies at the northern foot of the acropolis, and the steep, narrow tiers of seats were carved from the rock itself. After the middle of the day the seats are in the shade, and seen from the modern road appear to have faded back into the grey rock from which they were once cut. The only colour is a patina of red from the patches of old lichen. The tiers are divided into three blocks; at the very top a passage runs around the theatre in the vertical face of which there was an inscribed dedication, still visible at the beginning of the nineteenth century but now disappeared, to 'Laurel-bearing Apollo and Safe-giving Artemis'. There was no elaborate stage, and the spectators could look out northwards

---

†This side was particularly vulnerable to attack since a long ridge here extends to the west. At an earlier date the whole ridge was fortified. Walls of differing degrees of regularity extend in a large semi-circular sweep from the northwest corner of the later circuit out to the edge of a small valley and back again to the tower at the southwestern corner of the acropolis.

across the plain to the mountains of Opuntian Locris reddening in the afternoon light.

Once a year the stone seats of the theatre are again brought to life and coloured in by spectators when for a couple of evenings in early June a festival is held in honour of Plutarch. On one occasion I watched a production of Sophocles' *Antigone*. Earlier the programme had included traditional dancing warmly applauded by the large audience which spilled over the sides of the theatre and climbed up the rocks of the acropolis. From our seats of stone or rock we looked over the valley of the Cephisos to the purple hills of Locris as the sky turned a rich pink in the west. Then after speeches by several local and national officials in that eulogistic tone reserved for Greek public pronouncement the play at last began. It was not long after the ending of the dictatorship of Ioannides, and the audience was quick to see the modern parallels of the play. In the festive atmosphere the authoritarian Creon was booed, while Antigone and Haemon (Creon's defiant son) were cheered. Finally in the gathering darkness the audience listened in total silence to the news of the tragic deaths of Antigone and Haemon. The identity between actors and audience, between past and present seemed complete — until we left our cold seats and the theatre fell asleep under the summer stars.

5

THE SCHIST ROAD

The city of Chaironia was in antiquity the last Boeotian city before Phocis, which then lay principally to the south and east of Parnassos and included all the cities along the valley of the Cephisos. We noticed earlier the importance of Chaironia in guarding the passage through to central Greece from the north, but the city also guarded the passes into Boeotia from the territory of the Phocians — and the two were jealous neighbours. The Boeotians and Phocians had ended by fighting on opposite sides at the battle of Plataia, and although later in the fifth century they both sided with Sparta in the great war against Athens we have also seen how in the middle of the fourth century they were again involved in warfare. Partly this may have represented the differences between the populations of the two areas following the Dorian invasions, as reflected in their differing dialects. Partly too it might be characterised as the rivalry between men of the mountain and of the plain. For if the Athenians affected to find the Boeotians boorish it is not difficult to imagine how the inhabitants of the fastness of Parnassos must have appeared to a sophisticated Theban.

Of the ancient cities of Phocis none was of the first order of importance after the Mycenaean period. Yet each city had its own government and possessed its own fine walls. Collectively like the Boeotians the cities were enrolled in a confederacy, and the Phocian delegates met together in a large building called the Phocicon astride the Sacred Way to Delphi. Commanding the routes into central Greece both from the north along the Cephisos valley and from the Gulf of Corinth in the west the Phocians could hardly be disregarded. Moreover from this point the road to Delphi lay entirely within their territory.

It is an easy walk of about three-quarters of an hour from Chaironia to the village of Ayios Vlasios below the acropolis of ancient Panopeos, the first of the Phocian cities. The path starts from the handsome fountain constructed by the Turks from ancient materials situated near the theatre, and it runs westward all the way to Ayios Vlasios. At one time the first part of the route was paved and no doubt we are again following the old Turkish highway. After mounting a small ridge in the hills that here encroach into the plain, the path comes back down onto level ground at the mouth of the valley which lies to the east of Ayios Vlasios. This beautiful valley runs north-south and if followed leads to the village of Tsoukoulades near the modern Levadia-Delphi road. Its winter torrent is crossed here by a Turkish bridge. Ahead as you proceed there is a dramatic view of the citadel of Panopeos and of the rocks that form its natural defences on the eastern and along the entire northern flank; only on the other side was extensive walling necessary.

The path arrives in the small farming community of Ayios Vlasios at a large circular well (with basins set into the stone surround for use by animals) near the dilapidated cemetery and church of Ayios Nicolaos. The road ahead leads past the large church of the Metamorphosis to a small plateia with a couple of kafeneions. Travellers in the past have often noted the poverty of the village, making comparison with Pausanias when he calls Panopeos 'a city of the Phocians — if one can give the name of city to those who possess no government offices, no gymnasium, no theatre, no market-place, no water descending to a fountain, but live in bare shelters just like mountain cabins, right on a ravine'.†
The ancient traveller was clearly not impressed. For Panopeos had suffered worse than its other Phocian neighbours in previous centuries. Like them it had survived destruction by Xerxes and then a century and a half later by Philip, but it was again destroyed by the Mithridatic army in 86 BC and this time it never recovered. Some time afterwards the inhabitants abandoned the city and chose to live in 'bare shelters' under its shadow.

The poverty of Ayios Vlasios was still real enough in the last century, and Leake was here moved to comment on the oppression of the Greek farmers, under Turkish and Greek landlords alike. Indeed compared to its wealthier neighbour Davlia, the village remains relatively poor even today, with fewer tractors evident even allowing for the differing size of population and territory. A further indication is the small number of new concrete terrazas which increasingly disfigure the Greek villages. Here the houses

---

†Book X, 4.1, translated by W H S Jones (Loeb edition). The 'bare shelters' translate from the same work 'kaliva' that is used today to describe for example the Sarakatsani reed huts.

are still predominantly of whitewashed stone under pitched roofs of mellow clay tiles, and they spread out like a cluster of tiny farms, each with its own perivoli or small enclosure of land.

When I first arrived in the village square there were some elderly men sitting outside in the sunshine in loose relationship to a few tables from which the faded blue paint was almost visibly peeling. There was no sign of any cups or glasses, and I enquired if it was indeed a kafeneion. A slightly younger man who had been sitting with the others told me it was. He turned out to be the proprietor. He walked over to the table where I had seated myself and offered me a coffee. When the small cup arrived I started to pay. 'No, it's from us', the man said and sat down on the other side of the table. My payment was in the usual form — I had to satisfy the curiosity of the small audience by explaining where I came from and the rest. Later I asked about the village and was treated to a long account of the iniquities of the merchants who buy the products of the farmers at rock-bottom prices because they have a monopoly and then make huge profits on resale. It is a familiar enough complaint in the countryside and by no means confined to Ayios Vlasios. Yet the village possessed an atmosphere of despondency noticeable even before my perceptions were affected by the comments of earlier travellers. In the end I was pleased to leave such contemporary problems and make my way up the hillside to the kastro.

It is a stiff ten minute walk to reach the northwestern end of the citadel where there is a gap in the defences, or it takes a little longer to walk round the eastern end and enter by a gateway in the southern wall. Little sign remains now of the two walls which once ran down obliquely from either end of the acropolis to meet on the level, thus enclosing the ancient city. The top of the hill is almost encircled by a line of rocks. Along the northern side walling was only necessary in the gaps between the rocks, while on the southern side the crown of rocks is less evident and peters out altogether at the southwest so that the defences were here mostly dependent on man-made fortifications. Moreover particular care was needed in the construction of the walls on this southern side where, hidden from the village, a ridge joins the acropolis to the hills behind. The Greek engineers cleverly used both the rocks where they existed as well as the contours of the hill to enhance the effect of the fortification on the south. This wall is remarkably well preserved, particularly in its middle section. Constructed in the trapezoidal style already noted with some particularly large individual blocks, it rises to ten courses high for a long stretch with the remains of several towers, one of which — of thirteen courses high — is complete to the parapet. In places both faces of the wall can be seen and it is up to 4 metres thick. There are the remains of two gateways, the more easterly having the stone doorposts still visible.

Once on top of the hill the strategic importance of Panopeos' position is easy to grasp. Panopeos stands on the edge of the hills, isolated from them except by the ridge to the south and in control of the passes into and out of Phocis. Due north across the plain can be seen the narrow defile made by the Cephisos, at one time guarded by the city of Parapotamii, through which any invader from the north had to pass. Immediately below Panopeos the road to the west continued along the line of the Platania river towards the Schist Road and to the great cleft in the mountains between Cirphis and Parnassos (the Zemeno) that leads to present-day Arachova and to Delphi.

There is little of interest within the acropolis: the ruins of a mediaeval tower, a small chapel near two wells, a grove of holm oaks. But I well remember that first visit to Panopeos. It was a warm November day, the sky clear after the autumn rains. Wild cyclamen grew in the walls, and the tortoises were the only other visitors. Sitting up on the western tip of the acropolis I looked across to Davlia, which showed as a white scattering on the lower slopes of Parnassos. On the summit of the mountain the rain had laid a fine dusting of snow. In the plain below me a man was ploughing with a horse while others were sowing, broadcasting the seed from aprons at their waists. The newly ploughed soil alternated with the stubble, and a shepherd was driving his sheep across the golden patches, gleaning the last of the stalk. For a few moments time stood still in the sunshine, and it was possible falsely to imagine how life had always followed this peaceful pattern and how it always would.

By walking out of the gateway on the southwestern side you reach the ravine that lies along the western edge of the hill. Its slopes are formed of a reddish earth and it was probably here that Pausanias was shown the large clay-coloured stones said to be the remains of the clay from which Prometheus had made mankind. At the mouth of the ravine, close to the level plain, there is a small circular hillock which I presume is the mound which the ancient

traveller happily identified as the tomb of the giant Tityos who
Homer tells us had been killed by Apollo after he had violated the
god's mother, the nymph Leto, near Panopeos.

Homer gave to Panopeos the epithet 'kallichoros', describing the
beauty of its dancing floor, and Pausanias says he was puzzled by
this until it was explained to him by the Thyiads from Athens. It
was usual for the Thyiads to hold dances at places along the road
from Athens, and Panopeos was one of the venues; the poet was
probably referring to the dance of the Thyiads. And so long after
the city's decline, the young Athenian women on the way to Delphi
continued to stop here and to entertain the villagers with their gay
dithyrambs in return for the hospitality which they had
traditionally received since long before the now empty walls on the
acropolis hill had first been built.

*

For some time it was uncertain whether after Panopeos the
principal road to Delphi went across the plain to Davlia and along
the high route below Parnassos to the area of the Schist Road or
whether it followed the line of the Platania river into the valley of
Keresi where it joined the approximate route of the later Levadia-
Delphi road. The confusion was made greater by the varied
observations of modern travellers as to the number and direction of
roads or tracks visible at the famous junction of .the Schist Road
below Zemeno as if these were decisive of the ancient routes also.
What our guide has to say after he has visited Daulis from
Panopeos is as follows: 'Returning from Daulis to the direct road to
Delphi and proceeding forwards there is a building on the left of
the road called the Phocicon where the Phocian delegates
meet...Going on from here you will arrive at a road called the
Schist...'† Since the investigation in recent years of the scattered
ruins of a building in a field close to the Platania river, where it
flows through a defile between the outliers of Parnassos and the
lower slopes of Helicon into the Keresi valley, there is now no
longer any room for doubt as to the path of the ancient way. For
the scant ruins have been identified as almost certainly those of the
Phocicon. The Sacred Way clearly went not by Davlia but beside
the Platania river. Moreover the reason for this is obvious enough.

†Book X, 5.1–3

The route is both quicker and more level.

It is still possible to follow the route of a former road from Ayios Vlasios towards Keresi which I presume to be Turkish; like the road from Chaironia it probably lay close to the ancient way. While the direct path across the plain to Davlia (one and a half to two hours) leaves the village past a large group of cypresses, you take a path which diverges from it at the outset and goes slightly to the left. Once again there are signs of an old road under your feet — a fair sprinkling of even-sized stones. You aim for some cypresses in the middle of a very slight defile between two modest rises, scarcely hills, with that on the right having a white chapel upon it. After a time the path peters out, but you should continue in the same direction as you will suddenly find between two banks topped by holm oak the bed not of a stream but of an old road which runs over the top of the incline and directly down towards the Platania river. Although it disappears before reaching the river it would have crossed the Platania at a place where today at least it is easily fordable. On the further side of the river it could have joined the road from Davlia to Keresi, and there a path which local farmers say was paved by the Turks runs through the defile between the hills and past the ruins of the Phocicon.

On the road from Davlia to Keresi

This defile was of considerable importance in antiquity. It carried the main road to Delphi and also in effect joined the two parts of Phocis lying to west and east. It was the obvious place for the assembly house of the Phocians, and its ruins — a few blocks only apart from a profusion of tiles — lie in the middle of the defile to the left of the path from Davlia near a small white shrine. The remnants of the Phocicon hardly deserve attention, yet one can scarcely fail to be struck by the poignancy of such total destruction as well as by the beauty of its position sandwiched between the hills in this quiet valley. A short walk away on the other side of the path there is a grove of plane trees nurtured by a spring that issues mysteriously from underneath a large rock, its water like the melted snow of Parnassos. Here it is pleasant to rest in the shade beside the stream and savour the black taste of the spring water. From where you sit you can see opposite the spring a great rocky outcrop, the last bastion of Parnassos, commanding the entrance to the defile at its narrowest point. On the top are the ruins of a small Hellenic fort, probably once a guardpost and watchtower for the Phocian assembly. It is a difficult twenty-minute scramble up the goat tracks to reach the fort but the view is superb.

The road to Delphi passed under the fort and then entered the wide valley of Keresi on the further side of which, close under Helicon, runs the modern highway. The Platania river flows across the valley after emerging from a narrow defile to the west. It was through the length of this defile (Steno) that the ancient way had to pass, as did all later roads until the realignment of the route within the last few years. Some say that there are traces of the wheel-marks made by the passage of chariots in the Steno, but the only obvious sign of anything earlier than the metalled road is to be found on the left bank of the river at the beginning of the defile, where a broad track can still be seen running for some 50 to 100 metres before giving out. Again this was probably the Turkish road which then crossed the Platania to run along its right bank; most of its subsequent course would have been obscured by the impact of the first motor road built in 1931 which continued through the Steno. The only practical way to walk today is along the former motor route, which is peaceful enough now that the new highway diverts the traffic behind the hill of Kastri in the middle of the defile.

At the far end of the Steno it would have been necessary for earlier travellers to ford the river again before making across the valley that here opens between the height of Helicon, Cirphis and Parnassos. To the south the valley runs to Distomo, while ahead there is the cleft between Cirphis and Parnassos known as the Zemeno, up which the road to Delphi has to climb and from which the waters of the Platania flow down into the valley. The north of this bare valley is formed by the hill of Bardani, itself an outlier of Parnassos, and at the western end of Bardani there is a small rocky hillock behind which the upper road to Davlia proceeds. It is at this point, where the ancient roads from Daulis, Delphi and Lebadea (or Thebes) all met, that we can look for the legendary encounter of Oedipus and Laius. It is now known as the crossroads of Megas.

*

We have bypassed Davlia by following the 'direct' road to Delphi. Let us retrace our steps and like Pausanias cross the fields from the ruins of Panopeos to this most romantic of places. The village of Davlia lies under the great peaks of Parnassos and the houses straggle down a last spur of the mountain towards the olive groves

The acropolis of Davlia

and cornfields below. From this spur a ridge runs above a green valley to join the hill holding the ancient acropolis of Daulis, forming a huge horseshoe on the edge of the plain. The acropolis hill, isolated except for this connecting ridge, appears to swell from its base on the edge of the plain as if pregnant with some force still in the process of long gestation. Apart from where the grey rocks fall away sheer, particularly on the south and west, its whole rounded mass is draped with vegetation, olives at the lower level, then bushes of pournari and finally spiky pines over the summit. Even from a distance — and the kastro is no less striking when Davlia is approached by the small road off the main highway north from Levadia — the acropolis has a dark, brooding appearance. Closer at hand it possesses an atmosphere of mystery and wind-swept loneliness seldom encountered elsewhere.

According to mythology this was once the kingdom of Tereus. Tereus, a Thracian prince, was one of the first to suffer from the pollution of being served his own child to eat — an experience later shared by Thyestes the brother of Atreus with even more awful consequences. Tereus, like Thyestes, had been guilty of sexual misconduct. He was married to Procne by whom he had a son called Itys, but fell in love with Procne's sister Philomela. Having seduced Philomela the king cut out her tongue to prevent her revealing his crime and hid her away. However Philomela managed to inform Procne of her misfortune by weaving a message into a robe, and Procne in her desire to punish Tereus killed her son Itys and served his flesh to his father. When the king discovered what he was eating he rushed after the sisters to kill them. The gods then intervened; Tereus was turned into a hoopoe, Procne became a nightingale forever singing for her lost son, and Philomela a swallow. So goes this oddest of stories, and it is difficult to imagine more unfavourable origins for three of the most remarkable members of the bird kingdom. Yet it is a tale well suited to the romantic atmosphere of Daulis.

The site of the ancient city (known variously as Daulis or Daulia) lay below the southeast side of the acropolis where the road from the Phocicon would have approached it most quickly. At this point a number of hewn stones are visible in the earth, and this whole area is known as Lithari (Stone) thus indicating the site of the ancient city.

My guide to these few vestiges of Daulis was an elderly Davliot, a retired lawyer called Nikos Liberis, who played the role of local historian. Nikos, armed with a stout stick, forced his bulky frame along the muddy track from the village, and in his very correct Greek expounded his knowledge, occasionally poking me with his finger to make sure that I was taking in all he said. It was at Lithari that Nikos told me his understanding of the origin of the name Daulis or Davlia (as Daulia is now pronounced). Standing by a small shrine he indicated with his stick the point above a slight fold in the plain where the path turns down to Keresi. 'Here', he said, 'was a division in the ancient road from Panopeos. One route went to Tithorea, the other between the south side of the kastro and the neighbouring spur of Parnassos. It was in that valley that there was the Schist Road. There are traces of an old roadway in places, and it was higher up on that way where Oedipus killed Laius.' He was so positive that argument would be useless, even impolite. Clearly local pride required the Schist Road to pass Davlia.

'And the name?', I reminded him. The answer was ingenious. 'The name of Davlia', Nikos continued in the measured tones of a schoolmaster giving notes to a particularly dim pupil, 'the name Davlia comes from the word for the double flute, di-avlos, a flute which was made of two reeds with a single mouthpiece. That was the form of the division of the roads from Panopeos.'

So Nikos concluded and looked directly at me with an air that forbade any opposition.

However there is another version of the origin of the name of Davlia to be found in the village and one slightly nearer the truth. I was told this by Maria, a stumpy round-faced woman of forty, usually dressed in black, whose serious features could suddenly break out into the most infectious of smiles. One evening as I sat in her kitchen, while her old mother was stretched out asleep on the iron bed beside the fire, I asked her to tell me about the old city and how Davlia came by its name.

'The ancient city', she started, 'was on the hill below the kastro. Some years ago a man who only died recently found a tomb there with a gold sceptre in it. He was a poor man and after he found the tomb he kept quiet and went away to Germany. But when he came back he bought a house and olive trees and many stremmata of fields, and he began to talk about the find he had made before he left. That is how we know about the ancient city.'

This was a new variation on an old theme well known in this part of Greece. Usually the search for buried treasure is more familiar than its discovery. There are tales of secret digs for the gold chariot which was reputedly buried with Laius. Then gold sovereigns, said to have been parachuted to the andartes in the last war and carefully concealed against the Germans, provide more scope for fertile imagination. Another theme concerns the foreign archaeologist who, taken to see a tomb or inscription discovered by a local shepherd or farmer, steals away with the treasure, leaving the finder unrewarded. So it goes on, but on this occasion according to the story a Davliot had benefited from his find.

Maria continued. 'When the Turks came, the village was in the same place as the ancient city. It had elata (firs) among it, and there were also elata on the hill where the village is now. The Turks burnt the village and all the elata. All that was left was the trunks which were known as 'davloi' (firebrands). That is how the new village came to have the name of Davlia.'

This was not altogether correct as of course the name goes back to antiquity, but it struck a common chord with something in Pausanias. The ancient guide, in addition to giving the stock derivation of the name from the nymph Daulis who was the daughter of the local river, also attributes its possible origin to the word 'daula', used of heavily wooded places. As the modern word 'davlos' and the ancient word 'daula' are clearly closely related, it seems that the former explanation of the name has found its contemporary equivalent among the villagers, with the slight change in meaning between the two words affording a further opportunity to blacken the Turks.

It was in fact in the seventeenth century (some time after the first arrival of the Turks) that the village moved to its present position across the valley from the acropolis. One of the advantages of the site is the plentiful supply of water from Parnassos; it flows down the valley to form a tributary of the Platania, irrigating the fields as it passes, and on its way it is piped to the houses and fountains in the village. Like Levadia the water is a sufficient reason to guarantee settlement whatever disaster may occur. Under the Turks the population was Albanian, members of that hardy race driven south by the Ottomans in the fourteenth and fifteenth centuries. At the beginning of the last century when the village belonged to the Turkish ruler of Levadia, Dodwell was told it possessed sixty cottages and eighteen churches, although the latter were mostly so small that all except four escaped his notice. The traveller noted that 'the doors even of the better kind of churches are commonly so narrow as to admit only one person at a time, and this is done in order to prevent the Turks from converting them into stables'.† The writer goes on to describe a feast celebrated in the church on the acropolis. The villagers danced their way up to the acropolis, where they were all 'assembled in their gala dresses and passed the day in singing and dancing and eating boiled pulse mixed with dried currants'.

In 1826, during the War of Independence, after a stout defence the village was burnt by the Turkish force that was later destroyed at Arachova by Karaskakis. It was not to be the last time the village suffered. If we sometimes wonder at the relatively poor appearance today of many Greek villages and towns it is as well to remember the times they have endured destruction at the hands both of man and of nature; with existence seldom more than marginal there has until recently been little spare money for improvement. With recent history in mind it is also not too surprising if in new building preference is now given to flat-roofed concrete terrazas rather than to the traditional constructions in stone (or mud brick) and timber. Although they have spoilt the look of many villages, the new houses are more robust and less liable to be affected by fire and earthquake.

In 1943 Davlia was burnt by the Italians owing to the alleged presence of andartes, and nearly all its houses were destroyed. The Germans did little material damage — it is said they did not need to — although they did kill a number of young men as a reprisal. Then in the civil war the village suffered once again. It is estimated that at one time in the 'second war' (as it is called) there were some fifteen hundred rebels on Parnassos, and it was inevitable that Davlia as the largest village on the eastern side of the mountain would become involved. On one occasion the communists took and killed some of the leading figures of the village; on another the Greek army shelled the rebels in the village, killing a number of villagers including my friend Maria's sister and destroying a number of buildings.

Yet life had to continue. Maria's father-in-law, who was a muleteer, found that sometimes his animals were commandeered by the Greek army and at others by the rebels. Now his son, Maria's husband, owns a lorry and has been able to rebuild his father's house. Their income from the lorry is supplemented by the fields, mostly planted with olives, that came as Maria's dowry. The village

†Dodwell, *Tour* Vol. I, p. 202.

Tobacco crop at Davlia

begins to have an air of modest prosperity as it slowly renews itself, helped by its large landholding in the plain below and the additional income from work in the new factories established in Boeotia, including the huge aluminium plant at Aspra Spitia. The shops remain rudimentary — many of the villagers are virtually self-sufficent, and they will go to Levadia for any extra things they need — and the kafeneions in the large plateia, shaded by plane trees, are dark and at first sight depressing. Yet in the evenings the coffee-houses will fill, and the noise of the men's voices rises up the narrow street above the plateia like the sound of a great living machine at the heart of the village. Several hundred men sit here, noisily discussing business, contesting cards, or talking, endlessly talking, of football or politics. Every person is known to each other and many are bound by ties of family or obligation. Their world is as large or as small as the community itself. The old Phocian city of Daulis has become the Boeotian village of Davlia, but perhaps not everything has altogether changed.

Above the village of Davlia the road, which has wound up through the village from the plain, continues across upland pastures towards the crossroads of Megas and the old Schist Road. As it leaves the village it passes the small church of Ayios Minas in a prominent position overlooking the olive-filled valley below the acropolis. A little further on, near a shrine beside the road, a dirt track to the left leads along the ridge to the base of the kastro and from here a path indicated by a line of cypresses leads around a rocky spur towards the entrance. It was from this side that the citadel could most easily be approached and then only through a narrow defile below the walls, and it is difficult not to be impressed by the isolated grandeur of its position. The line of walls though ruinous may still be seen along the upper level of the rocks. The single gateway is flanked by the remains of an ancient quadrangular tower on one side and on the other by an inferior mediaeval structure built with small stones and infilled with bricks and mortar. Once inside, the uneven summit of the hill is found to be covered with trees and bushes forming a green canopy, which in spring and again in autumn is briefly variegated by a profusion of wild flowers. At the northeastern corner there are the ruins of the church of St Theodore, founded in the eleventh century by the Byzantine emperor Basil II 'the Bulgar-Slayer' to atone it is said for the blinding of ten thousand Bulgars (or nearly: ten he left with one eye each to lead their comrades home. When the mutilated survivors finally reached the Bulgar capital the sight so shocked their leader, Tsar Samuel, that he dropped dead on the spot, thus bringing the mediaeval Bulgarian kingdom to an end). With some difficulty owing to the undergrowth you can still trace the walls and towers around most of the circuit, chiefly in the style of the Macedonian rebuilding after Chaironia. Little else. Except a brooding, restless spirit, a strange blend of the sombre and the lyrical, well expressed in the figure of Philomela, singing for her dead son.

*

High up above the village of Davlia, at the base of a great grey ravine that carves through the southeastern face of Parnassos, there is a small cluster of red-tiled buildings standing out from the fir trees. It is the monastery of Jerusalem. Formerly it took about two hours to walk up the hillside from the village, and a route continued past the monastery up the ravine and then across the upper part of the mountain to Delphi. It was one way of reaching the summits of Parnassos and indeed Pausanias says that although longer than from Delphi the ascent by this way is less difficult.

Nowadays a dirt track (suitable for vehicles) leads from the metalled road all the way to the monastery, but few people choose to climb Parnassos from this side.

Many Greeks make the journey to the monastery in the summer months, often coming from far away, and then camp outside, even passing their holidays there. There are several such monasteries on Parnassos where the inmates may have dwindled in number or altogether disappeared, but which remain for the local villagers and other visitors places for periodic pilgrimage (most usually at the time of their festivals) and also centres for amenity during the summer months when their shaded positions have particular value. The expense of upkeep and improvement inevitably falls largely on the local communities, and these in turn retain some pride in their own particular monastery. In the case of the Jerusalem monastery (strictly a nunnery since 1967) its recent renovation has mostly been due to the unflagging efforts of its three nuns who have somehow succeeded in raising enough money for the rebuilding of many of the cells and other parts of the monastery.

The monastic buildings form a square, with the church in the middle, in the conventional manner. The foundation possibly dates back to the eleventh century, but later destruction (chiefly by the Turks in the War of Independence and by an earthquake in 1870) has left little of interest in what we see today. The nuns have nonetheless given charm to the courtyard by planting an abundance of flowers. The wing on the south side of the monastery provides rooms for the use of visitors, while the new north wing and the older east wing have the cells for the nuns whom the Mother Superior is sure will come. 'They will come', she declared as I sat with my friend Nikos the postman (last met at Thourion), who had delivered me up there on his weekly visit. We had been invited into a comfortable room in the south wing and there given in the manner so familiar to visitors to Mount Athos refreshment in the form of an ouzo, some loukoumi (Turkish delight) and a cup of coffee. When the Mother Superior then mentioned how much in debt the monastery was at that time owing to the cost of the new wing, Nikos immediately volunteered to give 10,000 drachmas of his own money to pay some of the most pressing debts until a further sum could be raised from the villages. The faith of the Mother Superior that one day more nuns would come and the building work be paid for was as unshakeable as her large comfortable presence.

The Monastery of Jerusalem

The church rebuilt in 1872 is of the usual cross-in-square form. The icons inside, including that of the Panagia to whom the monastery is dedicated, are said to be of the seventeenth century in the Cretan style. There is also a cabinet with several elaborate silver reliquaries, one containing the skull of St Dionysios, bishop of Corinth. Among other items there is a fine silver and gold cross of 1749 and two intricately carved wooden crosses encased in metal adorned with jewels.

The reason for the monastery bearing the name of Jerusalem remains uncertain. The most likely explanation is that it was either founded by a monk of Jerusalem, or it became a dependency of the monks of Jerusalem shortly after its foundation. Much later it did indeed become a dependency of an Eastern monastery, when in 1776 in order to escape the burdensome taxation of the Turks it adopted the expedient followed by many Greek monasteries of becoming a methochi of the famous monastery of St Catherine on Mount Sinai (Jabal Musa) which was itself exempt from taxation, and this dependency only finally ended in 1905.

There is an unflattering portrait of the monastery during the pre-revolutionary period painted by the traveller Clarke, who arrived here after descending from Parnassos. There were then fifty monks, whose 'state of ignorance did not differ from that of the other wild tenants of their lofty wilderness and [whose] simplicity was such as to excite the laughter even of our guides at every remark they made'.† After damning their 'heathen ceremonies' Clarke even suggests that not one of the monks could read or write. But his account is plainly exaggerated, whatever the shortcomings of some of the monks, since at this time the monastery provided a measure of Greek education, however rudimentary, for the local children. Later the monks played a heroic part in the War of Independence.

Despite destruction of its buildings during the war, the monastery still retained great wealth in the form of its lands, but some of this was then given by the government to other heroes of the struggle against the Turks and finally in 1928 most of the remaining land was expropriated. There is now left only a small amount of grazing land to provide any income apart from the money given by others.

At a short distance from the monastery there is a small cave situated near a spring. The icon of the Panagia which is now in the principal church is reputed to have been found there, and the cave has become a chapel. On the templon there are wall paintings in good preservation which are said to date from the seventeenth century, the same period as the icon. If you walk on past the cave and through the trees you reach a rocky platform surmounted by a

†*Travels* (1818), p. 269

large cross. From here there is a remarkable view over Boeotia to the mountains of Euboea beyond the Euripos. Below, round the edges of the fields on the huge plain, are scattered the villages — the descendants of the proud cities of antiquity. Like Christ you seem to see before you the kingdoms of the world: Daulis, Panopeos, Lebadea, Orchomenos and round to Elatia in the valley of the Cephisos. I like to think too that it was from here that Davellis, Christo-Davellis, surveyed his territory one July day in 1856.

*

Between Davellis, the Jerusalem monastery and the Megas cross-roads (from which we retraced our steps to Davlia) there is a connection. Part of the story of that connection no doubt belongs to the realm of myth and some of it belongs to history. Davellis was the leader of a band of brigands which like many others in the middle of the nineteenth century had come to terrorize large parts of central Greece. The area around Parnassos was a natural centre for their operations. To some extent the problem had existed since the end of the War of Independence when the klephtic tradition became a convenient cloak to hide the crimes of groups of men left rootless and unrewarded after the struggle against the Turks. In the middle of the century the problem became acute. After 1854, when at the time of the Crimean War the new kingdom of Greece had unsuccessfully sought with the help of irregulars to annex Thessaly and Epiros, which were not yet within its territory, 'the armed bands of criminals and brigands when driven back into Greece carried on the same system of plundering the agricultural population which the Greeks had dignified with the name of war when it was pursued in Turkey.'† There was virtual anarchy in the countryside and the government of King Otho was at last forced to act.

Ioannis Megas, a veteran of the war against the Turks who was then living at Arachova, was given command of the gendarmerie throughout central Greece, under the direct orders it is said of Queen Amalia herself. After successes against other bands, Megas went after Davellis who was in the area of Desphina with some twenty-four men. The bandit retired to Parnassos where on 14 July

†Finlay, *History*, Vol. VII, p. 227

he was in the vicinity of the monastery of Jerusalem. Here the tale can be taken up in the words of an old Davliot shepherd called Loukas who, forced into semi-retirement by arthritis, likes nothing better than the opportunity to retell such stories. Loukas had been describing to me the old custom of telling fortunes from the shoulder blade of a sheep, and he was reminded of the story of Davellis.

'Years ago', he had started, 'there were robbers in the area, bad men not like the klephts of old. They went up to the monastery and demanded some food, threatening that otherwise they would burn it all down. They were given some bread and they took the one sheep that the monks then possessed. The robbers went onto the hillside near the monastery and roasted the sheep. After they had finished eating Davellis took the shoulder blade and looked at it. He didn't like what he saw. "It foretells evil for us", he said to the others, "we must leave here at once". Straightaway they hastily departed, and made for the Zemeno. Meanwhile the monks whose faith in the Panagia had been disturbed by the loss of their sheep took her icon out of the monastery and threatened to burn it unless it would perform a miracle.'

'Did a miracle occur?' I was forced to ask.

'Yes it did, for what could be more miraculous than that the robbers left Parnassos where they would never have been caught and went down to the hill at the crossroads of Megas where they were easily surrounded. The next day they were all killed except one.'

For Loukas, knowing Parnassos as he does, it was obvious. When the brigands could have roamed over the entire mountain above the monastery, their lunatic course of flight to the Zemeno could only have been caused by an act of God. In this way the bare facts of Davellis' visit to the monastery and his death at the crossroads have been elaborated in the popular imagination.

Ioannis Megas who was responsible for surrounding Davellis' band was himself killed in the attack. A cross inscribed with a bare recital of Megas' death on 15 July now surmounts the small rocky hill at the base of the Zemeno. Since that time these famous crossroads have been known as the crossroads of Megas, and if Davellis has entered into local myth Megas too has been celebrated in popular songs. Nor did Queen Amalia forget her officer — she is said to have given his family a pension from her own funds and even to have planted the plane tree at the old Khan of the Zemeno in his memory.

*

The crossroads of Megas was the scene of another fateful encounter, this time entirely mythical. I refer to the meeting of Oedipus and Laius. Pausanias gives us some of the topographical detail. 'Going forward from here (the Phocicon) you will come to a road called the Schist Road. It was on this road that Oedipus killed his father...The Schist Road and the rash deed Oedipus there committed were the beginning of his troubles, and the tombs of Laius and the servant who followed him are just as they were in the very middle of the place where the three roads meet and over them have been piled unhewn stones...From here the highway to Delphi becomes uphill and more difficult even for an active man.'†
The three roads we infer from Sophocles' *Oedipus Tyrannos* were the roads from Delphi, Daulis and Thebes. The only possible junction of those roads which also fits Pausanias' description is the crossroads of Megas. In this lonely landscape, at the base of the long defile between Parnassos and Cirphis, we can then place the meeting of Laius with Oedipus, 'the beginning of his troubles'.

The myth of Oedipus follows us at almost every step of the road from Cithairon to Delphi and perhaps it is worth recalling in some detail. It must be seen particularly in the context of the Delphic oracle which from its prominence in the story must have played a part in fashioning the myth as we know it. One of the most frequent enquiries at Delphi concerned the prospect of a marriage or of the birth of children. In the latter case Laius, the childless king of Thebes, received the reply that he would have a child but that he would die at its hands. When his wife gave birth the king took the baby and having nailed its feet together exposed it to die on Mount Cithairon.

The baby was found on the mountain by a Corinthian shepherd who named him Oedipus, Swell-Foot, and the child was then adopted by the King and Queen of Corinth. When Oedipus grew up he travelled to Delphi to enquire from the oracle who were his true parents. There he was rudely told that he would kill his father and (in some accounts) marry his mother. The identity of his true parents was not told him, and so wishing to avoid his adoptive parents he turned his back on the Corinthian Gulf and left Delphi

†Book X, 5.3–4. The 'Schist Road' probably had the meaning of the 'Branching Road'.

in the direction of Thebes. On the Schist Road he met king Laius who in turn was on his way by chariot to Delphi to enquire how to rid the country of the Sphinx. At the crossroads Laius ordered the younger man out of his way and after a brief altercation Oedipus killed Laius and his servant. He then continued on his way to Thebes where after successfully solving the riddle of the Sphinx he became king and was given the hand of the widowed queen Jocasta. The remaining part of the tale is told by Sophocles: how when Thebes is troubled by plague the Delphic oracle is consulted yet again and prescribes that the murderer of Laius must be expelled from the city; how Oedipus eagerly seeks the murderer only to discover by degrees that it is in fact himself; and how finally in the awful knowledge of their true relationship his mother hangs herself and Oedipus then puts out his eyes with her brooch.

Our picture of Greece — both as it is and as it was — is so suffused with light, it is painted with such vivid colours and the details etched so sharply (even if inaccurately) that we easily forget to notice the inevitable shadows concealed behind the sunlit contours, the dark troughs of suffering and the burdens of guilt. We survey the entire period of Greek history. Our eyes focus on the clean white marbles of antiquity, the glittering mosaics of Byzantium or the pallikar crouched in his ambuscade picking off the turbaned Mussulman. Naturally we select the glorious and exclude the dark episodes from our gaze. We do not like to dwell on the successive legions of foreign invaders or on the self-inflicted wounds — the blood-letting in the massacres at Plataia and Melos, the butchery in the War of Independence or again during the recent civil war. But there has always been this tragic vein in Greek experience, and it is something of which the ancient Greeks were profoundly aware. They saw it most clearly in the case of individuals. Even the most conspicuously successful mortal could suddenly be struck down by a malignant fate. There was no shortage of examples. Like Croesus, a most generous benefactor at Delphi, who nonetheless lost his entire empire. And Oedipus, whose world crumbled away in a few moments of self-discovery. In the end Oedipus discovered that all his successes had been based upon illusion. He blinded himself because he had been betrayed by the world which he saw and thought he knew.

Deep to the very founts of sight
He smote, and vowed those eyes no more should see

The wrongs he suffered, and the wrong he did.
'Henceforth', he cried, 'be dark — since ye have seen
Whom ye should ne'er have seen, and never knew
Them that I longed to find.' So chanted he,
And raised the pins again, and yet again,
And every time struck home.†

The ancients viewed Oediupus as a real historical figure of the past. Pausanias even tells us that he saw the tomb of Laius in the very middle of the crossroads, 'where the three roads meet'. We are bound to wonder what it was the writer was describing. There are those who in the past have looked for the tomb on the level ground at the base of the Zemeno, forgetting that we are dealing with mythical characters and a naive observer. I think there can be little doubt that Pausanias was talking of the hill where Davellis was cornered by Megas — what we might call the Megas hill. For as you walk down the Zemeno, or indeed as you come along the direct road from Davlia, the Megas hill projecting from the end of the hill of Bardani does indeed appear to occupy the middle of the area where the three roads meet. Moreover the rocky outcrop does give the impression of a pile of unhewn stones just as Pausanias says he saw heaped over the tombs of Laius and his servant. Here then is the tomb of Oedipus' father, but you will seek in vain for his golden chariot.

†Sophocles, *Oediupus Tyrannos*, lines 1270–1276, translated by J T Sheppard

6

SAINT LUKE OF STIRIS

One of the songs remembering Megas and Davellis starts by telling us how the robber has devastated the three villages of Arachova, Distomo and Davlia. Their names make a pleasant consonance. It was from these villages which lie in opposite directions from the Megas crossroads that the officer summoned additional help before making his final assault. Davlia we have visited, Arachova lies on the way to Delphi and Distomo we shall visit on the way to the monastery of St Luke. It is a diversion from our journey to Delphi but an inevitable one.

The small town of Distomo is pleasantly situated among low hills at the south of the valley that runs away from the Megas hill. To the east is Mount Helicon and to the north Cirphis, their flanks scarred by the red tracks made by machinery exploiting the large deposits of bauxite, the raw material of aluminium; from here large lorries carry the red earth to the vast aluminium factory on the coast in the bay of Anticyra. The town itself has a dusty, semi-derelict air. The buildings along the principal streets and in the plateias through which the road passes have little character. There is a historical reason for this which we shall shortly discover, but there are still some rewards behind the first dirty layer. And the people of Distomo are kindly, determined to efface the bitter memory of one of the most barbaric episodes of the last war.

The town has rightly achieved a notoriety for what occurred on 10 June 1944. It is known simply as the Sphagi, the Slaughter, and it happened in this way. On that particular day the German occupation forces had been searching for andartes, the Greek resistance, first in Distomo and then in the nearby village of Stiri. There they encountered the Greeks and in the ensuing fight the Germans lost one of their officers. Returning to Distomo towards nightfall the Germans set about killing every inhabitant they could find — men, women and children. It is said that only one person was spared, an old woman who had offered a German some water. Fortunately many of the Distomites were able to escape as darkness fell, but no less than 229 Greeks were slaughtered. A large plaque hangs in the portico of the Metropolitan church of

Ayios Nicolaos in the central plateia, recording the names and ages of the victims. It includes over forty children under ten years of age, the youngest being two months old. The Germans left after burning many of the houses. For some three months afterwards the Greeks stayed away from Distomo, living in the hills. When they returned they painted blue crosses by the doors of the houses of the victims.

The agony of Distomo did not end there, for a second plaque next to the other tells us that some twenty-three Distomites were killed by the communists between 1944 and 1949, including the proedros of the community. It was only after the civil war that with aid from the Americans Distomo was able to begin rebuilding. For this reason the central plateia is named after an American, President Roosevelt.

A few of the older houses still remain along the street that runs from the Plateia Roosevelt up to the small circular hill on the north side of the town which is surmounted by the church of Ayios Elias. This hill is almost certainly the site of the acropolis of the ancient city of Ambrossos, and the church possibly stands on the site of a temple. To the west there is an associated hill, also circular in form, around which can be traced in parts the remains of the former city walls.

*

Few people would come to Distomo if it did not lie on the way to the monastery of Osios Loukas, one of the most famous Byzantine monuments in Greece. Beyond Distomo the road goes through the small farming village of Stiri, and after the turning down for Kiriaki it follows a line of hills jutting out into a large basin formed between the surrounding heights of Helicon, before finally it arrives through almond groves above the monastery itself.

The Greeks say that the monks have kept all the best sites for themselves, and in the case of Osios Loukas it is difficult to disagree. It lies on a platform halfway up the hillside and overlooks to the east an extensive valley, a changing tapestry of cornfields and pasture painted with the red of the bauxite earth and the green of olives and almond trees and of bushes of pournari, all cradled below the wooded slopes of Helicon. To the southeast, in the middle of the valley, you can see a long tabular hill with a ring of rocks running around its flat summit. This is known as Palaiochora and was once the acropolis of the Phocian city of Stiris which then possessed this beautiful valley. Ancient Stiris gave its name to the hill where the monastery is situated as well as to the village to the west, and St Luke himself became known as St Luke the Stiriote, after he had spent the last years of his life in this remote corner. It was in honour of St Luke the Stiriote that a church was later built which is perhaps the finest Greek church after that of Santa Sophia at Istanbul.

We know a considerable amount about St Luke (who is not to be confused with the Evangelist) and how he came to live here. His biography was written within a few years of his death by an anonymous monk who probably knew Luke personally. It appears from the biography that Luke was born on 29 July 896 at Kastri (Delphi). His family was well-to-do and had originally come from Aegina. From an early age Luke marked himself apart from his brothers and sisters by preferring an ascetic and religious life, and at the age of fourteen he became a hermit at Ioannitsa on the deserted promontory of Makrinikola south of Desphina, where he remained for seven years. While he was there the story is related how two monks passing on the way to Rome gave him a monk's

The Monastery of Osios Loukas

habit. There Luke might have stayed but for the Bulgarians under Tsar Simeon who in 917 swept down to the shores of the Gulf of Corinth. Luke is said to have escaped by swimming across the Gulf to the Peloponnese where he spent ten years serving a stylite near Patras, providing his food and water. On Simeon's death in 927 peace was made with the new Bulgarian monarch and Luke was able to return to Ioannitsa. He stayed there for twelve years until his growing fame caused him to go to the tiny harbour of Kalami on the bay of Anticyra for the sake of greater privacy. Later owing to the inroads of further invaders from the north he was forced to take refuge on the small barren island of Ambelos, in the bay of Anticyra. It was finally in 945 that Luke arrived at Stiris, and on the hillside where the monastery was later built, near a spring, he made his garden — 'a true paradise both in its produce and its appearance' — and nearby he made his cell. In the cell Luke dug a small pit like a grave where 'to keep his mind on death he slept little and continually sang and prayed'.

However the ascetic was no longer alone. He was attended by several disciples, and received many visitors. One of these was the Byzantine commander of Greece, Crinites, who started to build here a small church of Ayia Varvara. Luke had acquired by now a considerable reputation as a wonder-worker. He was accredited with many miracles of healing, was said to converse with animals like St Francis of Assisi, and even possessed powers of prophesy; he allegedly foretold the invasion of the Bulgars under Simeon as well as the eventual recapture of Crete (which occurred in 961, after his death). In this latter respect it may be no coincidence that Luke who had been born at Delphi and lived most of his life near that ancient centre of prophecy was reputed to have such qualities. It suggests that he was particularly well qualified to assert the power of the new religion over that of the old.

Luke died at the age of fifty-six on 7 February 953, just as the blossom was coming on the almond trees. He was quickly recognised as a saint and, according to the biography, two years after his death some of his disciples finished the church of Ayia Varvara, made the cell where he had been buried into a chapel, and built cells for themselves and their visitors. On this account therefore the monastery was founded in about 955.

However the foundation of the monastery should be totally distinguished from the foundation and building of the great Church of Osios Loukas. Although this edifice has been dated on stylistic grounds to the first part of the eleventh century (as have the mosaics), its construction is the subject of many conflicting traditions of imperial benefaction. In addition there are the further questions of the date of the Panagia (the smaller building alongside Osios Loukas) and of the precise correlation between on the one hand the two churches which we see today and on the other the original church of Ayia Varvara and the chapel built over the saint's tomb. None of these questions is easy to answer.

The most persistent tradition, recorded in an eighteenth century manuscript at the monastery but well established by the time of Spon and Wheler's visit in 1676, associates the building of the church of Osios Loukas with the recapture of Crete in 961, which occurred under the reign of emperor Romanos II and which the saint is said to have predicted twenty years earlier. According to this tradition the emperor and his wife Theophano built the church out of gratitude for the saint's successful prophecy, sending an army of craftsmen from the capital to the site of the monastery. Here they found a church next to the saint's tomb (which we infer to be that of Ayia Varvara) and tearing this down they built 'the new Sion' in its place. This tradition does not however explain how the Church of the Panagia came to be built. For it was demonstrated in 1964 that the Panagia is earlier in date than the larger church, since it was found that the south wall of the Panagia had been used to form part of the north wall of the Katholicon. Nor does foundation by Romanos square with the saint's biographer who writing after 961 speaks of the fulfillment of the saint's prophesy concerning Crete without mentioning the building of a new church — despite the fact that if the tradition were correct the work must have begun before 963 when Romanos died. In addition the tradition was not that told to Cyriacus of Ancona when he visited the monastery in 1436 and himself inscribed in Latin, on a wall used by way of a visitor's book, that the church had been built by (Constantine) Monomachos who was emperor from 1042 to 1054.

However even if the emperor Romanos had nothing to do with the church of Osios Loukas, the fact remains that this rich building could only have been an imperial foundation among several others built at the time of renaissance and reform under the Macedonian dynasty. During this period, although the foundation and building of monasteries was interrupted from time to time by Bulgarian invasions into the empire, such troubles only acted as a fresh stimulus to reassert the orthodox religion in the face of heterodoxy in all its forms. One example of imperial patronage was that of the emperor Constantine Monomachos who was responsible for the building of Nea Moni on Chios. The name of Constantine has also been connected with Osios Loukas and it is possible that he may have been responsible for some part of the completion of the church in Phocis such as the marble or mosaic decoration. But there remains a better candidate for the substantial part of the work, namely Basil II 'the Bulgar-Slayer'. Basil, the son of Romanos II and Theophano, was emperor from 976 to 1025. It was he who won the final victory over the Bulgars in 1014 and, although there can be no certainty, it was probably he who commissioned the great new church of Osios Loukas in celebration of his own victories and also in memory of those of his father in Crete (hence the traditional association of Romanos with the building of the church). This foundation by Basil II is consistent with the stylistic dating of the building to the early eleventh century and also with one other clue — an incomplete and enigmatic inscription built into the church of St Luke at Aliveri in Euboea. This church was a metochi or dependency of the monastery of Osios Loukas and it possessed certain close similarities in its decoration with those of the larger church of St Luke. The inscription while mentioning the names of both Basil and Constantine (probably Basil's brother, Constantine VII, emperor 1025–1028) gives the date of the foundation of that building as 1014. This might suggest a very similar date for our church. Finally Basil may even have visited the new building in 1018 when he was travelling through Greece on his way to dedicate votive offerings to the Panagia in the converted Parthenon at Athens. We know that he stayed at Levadia and it would have been natural for him to have gone to see for himself the progress being made on the latest ornament to God's empire on earth.

In summary then, according to the Life of Saint Luke the monastery was first founded in about 955 shortly after the saint's death. At that time the monks completed the church of Ayia Varvara and built a chapel over the tomb of the saint. The great church of Osios Loukas was built later and is to be assigned to the first part of the eleventh century, commissioned by the emperor Basil II though possibly not completed until after his death, perhaps by Constantine Monomachos. The tradition that the new church was built in the place of Ayia Varvara may well be correct, since the crypt of Osios Loukas (while undoubtedly constructed at the time of the new building) retains the name of Ayia Varvara. The existing church of the Panagia, which is to be dated at least in part prior to the building of Osios Loukas, may then represent the original oratory over the tomb of the saint as subsequently altered or rebuilt to allow for a better architectural relationship with the newer church.† In this respect it may be highly significant that the relics of the saint were eventually placed in the north transept of the larger church which could be reached directly from the Panagia and indeed which remained from an architectural point of view strictly part of the exo-narthex of the smaller church, thus effecting a compromise between the claims of the two buildings.

Outside the monastery itself a large terrace shaded by a spreading plane tree leads to the principal entrance which is formed by a fine vaulted gateway. This gate was once guarded by a tower which was converted into the belfry in the nineteenth century, and this together with the remains of the walls on the south and east may help to remind us that in the Middle Ages the monastery had something of the aspect of a small fortified town. The cells on the west and north, and the walls on the other two sides with their accompanying buildings, created an enclosure around the two principal structures in the centre — the churches of Osios Loukas (the Katholicon) and the Panagia. Within the walls of the monastery there was spring water and also ample space for the storage of food from its extensive lands. History does not show us that these defensive qualities were ever of much avail against the customary ravages by the Franks and the Catalans, and later the Albanians and the Turks — except on the famous occasion in 1780, when for twelve days the elder Androutsos withstood seige by a Turkish army before making a bold escape with all his men. Nonetheless it was here, as we saw earlier, that Bishop Isaias proclaimed the outset of the revolution in 1821 (remembered by a plaque on the terrace) and the monastery remained throughout the struggle a centre of operations and a source of supply for the revolutionaries. Today the atmosphere is peaceful, as if the monastery, without any enemies except indifference, has finally withdrawn from the world. The few remaining monks are occasionally seen flitting like spectres along the terraces or across the courtyard into the small church of the Panagia, which alone of the two churches is still used for worship. Like the Katholicon itself

†This would account for the peculiarity of the axis of the Panagia.

The two churches of Saint Luke (left) and the Panagia (right)

the monastery has become little more than a museum.

The central position of the two churches within the monastery, and their relationship to each other, can be better appreciated by first walking under the arched buttresses between the Katholicon and the refectory and thus approaching the eastern ends of the buildings. Here from the other part of the courtyard you see the external facades of their apses, with that of the Panagia projecting further than Osios Loukas to reflect the manner in which the west end of the smaller church is set back behind the larger. From this (east) side the smaller, more delicate cupola of the Panagia contrasts with the more substantial, squat dome of the Katholicon and any tendency towards symmetry within the overall harmony of the two buildings has been further avoided by the variation in the decorative patterns of the brickwork and by the more lavish windows of the larger church. Another feature particularly evident here is the quantity of ancient material used in the lower courses of both buildings, and it is also very noticeable in the nearby north gateway. This has almost certainly come from the ancient structures still to be seen on the hillside both above and below the monastery. These ruins belonged to a fortress, probably constructed in this important position by the nearby city of Stiris.

Before entering the Katholicon you might look more closely at its windows. Of those at the lower level some are still walled up from the days of the fighting against the Turks and most of the others have stone slabs of recent date, pierced with holes to admit the light. Originally however, as we can see from the higher level, the pierced slabs (then made of plaster) were confined to the upper part of the window while the lowest part was filled with a thin almost transparent section of marble carved with reliefs showing Byzantine motifs of foliage and animals; in between the two (where now there is glass) there were usually shutters, again perhaps of very thin marble. The effect of these exquisite windows would have been to filter a soft, yellow light into the interior of the church which only enhanced the mystery of the ritual and the richness of the decoration.

Inside the building the light is still subdued. The walls and the floor are covered with slabs of marble of varying hues, of green, yellowish-white, blue-grey, red and cipollino, placed in sections between contrasting borders. These marble linings were the work or gift (it is unclear which) of a monk called Gregory, and it is to this otherwise unknown figure that we owe much of the satisfying effect of the interior, as the soft colours of the marble bestow upon it an uncomplicated and unifying richness. Another immediate impression is made by the elaborately carved iconostasis screening the sanctuary, from which the sixteenth century icons of Christ and the Panagia, painted against gold, appear to gather up the light in the half-darkness and then radiate it directly back at the spectator. Other details catch the eye also: the frieze patterned in black and white marble that runs round three sides of the building; the carved slabs similar to those in the window openings fencing in the gallery; then at a higher level the ornamental string-course of acanthus leaves and astragali, and around the springing of the arches a circular cornice of similar form. But as your eye travels upwards it is struck by decoration of a different order. There on the curved surfaces of the ceilings, on the soffits of the arches, in the apse, on pendentives, in the transepts, in recesses and vaults, mosaics glow from a gold background — a concourse of saints and martyrs, a Biblical thesaurus presided over by the figures of Christ and the Mother of God. Only in the dome itself do the mosaics fail, having fallen in the sixteenth century, and here faded wall-paintings replace the original decoration.

The domed cross-in-square church, which developed in the ninth

century after the end of the iconomachia, was particularly well
suited to such decorative effect. The Byzantine architects had
succeeded in resolving a square ground plan into a circular dome by
the use of arches and pendentives or squinches, and by this means
the weight of the dome could be carried down onto piers or pillars
and then spread throughout the building by the arches and vaults
below. The architectural virtue of the plan was that the building
was self-supporting without need of external buttressing,† but
another great advantage was the scope it gave to Byzantine artists
to create within this enveloping space, particularly on the many
curved surfaces, a decorative scheme illustrative of God's universe.
Osios Loukas is one of the earliest examples of this scheme, which
later developed into an arrangement laid down precisely in the
Byzantine *Painter's Guide*. In the summit of the dome, Christ the
Pantocrator rules from heaven. Around him are his Mother, his
Messenger (John the Baptist) and the four Archangels. Below,
between the windows of the drum, are the sixteen Prophets who
foretold his coming. Then the semi-circular pendentives show
some of the principal scenes from his life: the Annunciation
(replaced by fresco), the Birth, Purification and Baptism, all
illustrative of major festivals in the liturgical year. On the soffits of
the main arches we see the greater warrior saints accompanied by
Christ and by the Archangels Michael and Gabriel, and on this
same general level, on the ceiling of the sanctuary, there is a
representation of Pentecost, while in the apse we see the Mother of
God with the infant Jesus.

Below this more exalted plane comes an army of saints and
martyrs, among them a large number of bishops and hermits: in
the transepts, in the vaults on either side of the vestibule (where in
the corners owing to lack of light frescoes were used instead of
mosaics) and in the parabemata on either side of the sanctuary. In
four recesses at the angles of the central square of the church and
thus in positions of great importance at this level, are the four Fathers
of the Eastern Church, St Gregory the Wonderworker, St Nicolas, St
Basil (the founder of Orthodox monasticism) and St John
Chrystostom. Below these great pillars of the Church, and
deliberately distanced from them by the panels of marble, the earthly
faithful might worship under the scrutiny of God himself.

† The great buttresses on the south of the church of Osios Loukas can only
be due to the slope of the hillside.

Such is the general scheme of the decoration of Osios Loukas, except that it makes no mention of the narthex where in fact the mosaics may be seen to their very best effect.† Here too despite the limitations imposed by the uniform height, there is still a hierarchy among the figures. The portrait of Christ enjoys the most prominent position over the doorway, while the medallions of the Mother of God, St John the Baptist and the two Archangels occupy the vault nearest to him. Important scenes from the Bible occupy the adjacent walls: the Washing of Feet, the Crucifixion, the Resurrection and the Doubting of Thomas. The soffits of the arches between the vaults are occupied by the twelve Apostles (who turn slightly in the direction of Christ), and the two remaining vaults as well as the west wall have figures or medallions of saints. The scenes and figures are divided from each other by bands of beautiful floral and geometric design, similar to those used in the principal part of the church but more striking when seen close at hand. As a whole the decoration represents the perfect conjunction between the Byzantine liking for abstract or floral patterns, so well developed during the period of iconoclasm, and their passionate interest in portraying religious figures, which was now at last recognised as legitimate after the restoration of Orthodoxy by the empress Theodora in AD 843.

The description of the scheme of mosaics already suggests a deeper purpose than mere embellishment. In representing the universe of God from Christ in heaven to the saints on earth and in recalling scenes from the Incarnation and Passion of Christ it was intended to illustrate both the liturgy and the great festivals of the Byzantine church. The building and its decoration were designed to become one with the mysteries celebrated within it. This had a practical as well as a liturgical significance. For the ordinary worshipper, uneducated and in any event without access to the very limited number of manuscript texts of the Bible, the pictures in the church told the story of Christ and of the trials and triumphs of his Church which he could not know from elsewhere. Here was the Orthodox faith described in picture book form. It was the great supporter of icons, John of Damascus, who said 'If a pagan asks you to show him your faith, take him into church and place him before the icons'.

_____

†A more precise identification of the subject matter of the mosaics and frescoes is to be found in Appendix II.

There was of course always a danger in the representation of holy or divine figures, namely that the images themselves might become the objects of worship, particularly as some were accredited with miraculous powers. It was the problem of idolatry that had sparked off the controversy of the icons, the iconomachia, which lasted from the early eighth century to the middle of the ninth. During most of that time all icons were forbidden.

John of Damascus was the man who found the theoretical justification for icons. He developed the Neoplatonist theory that such visible forms are the only way that we can appreciate, and thereby reach, the absolute or divine. The images of Christ are simply a route by which we can approach him — 'Christ is venerated not in the image, but with the image'. The argument is similar in the case of the images of the saints and even their relics. For these merit reverence as in some way partaking of the divine principle which had earlier inspired the saints' lives. It is an attractive solution to the difficulties presented by icons and one which had considerable impact on Byzantine art. Yet I suspect it has had only limited effect on the minds of most followers of Orthodoxy. For all the ecclesiastical disapproval of idolatry and the theoretical view of the use of icons they appear to answer a fundamental need felt especially by the Greeks to have and to see their gods and saints in physical proximity to them. Few perhaps literally worship the images themselves, but the representations are required as tangible proofs of the existence of the divine world. The desire for seeing and communing with God and the saints can be satisfied in large measure by the contemplation of their images in churches and elsewhere, and it may not be too fanciful to suppose that the same spirit and the same reason led their ancestors to place around the walls of their temples and above the portals representations of gods and heroes in friezes, metopes and pediments.

For the spectator these figures of history or myth form part of a population of beings, which while belonging to another world still remain with one foot firmly in this through the medium of their physical representations. It is one of the reasons why Greeks still have such a liking for stories of the presence on earth of the divine or the supernatural. In many cases there is no deeper purpose than simply to keep such things before our eyes.

*

I remember one such story, though it has very little to do with
Osios Loukas. It was told me by the saint's namesake, the arthritic
shepherd at Davlia. In their small livingroom Loukas' daughter was
burning some incense, as she does every night, 'for the icon'. This
icon is a small reproduction on cardboard of the Panagia and it sits
on a shelf in the corner of the room next to an oil lamp. Loukas was
reminded of a story about livani (incense) which he cleverly grafted
onto what I had told him of my search that afternoon for some
blackberries.

'Once', he started off, 'there were two shepherds, one intelligent
and one stupid. By chance they found some livani. The intelligent
one of the two took away his share to sell it while the stupid
shepherd built a fire and threw the incense on the flames. Now the
Panagia was in a nearby cave, not feeling at all well. When she
smelt the incense she immediately recovered and she sent an angel
to find out who was burning it. The angel returned with the
shepherd. "Why were you burning the incense when you might
have sold it like the other shepherd?" the Panagia asked. The
shepherd told her that he liked the smell. The Panagia was pleased
with his answer and asked him what she could give him. "A
clarinet", he said, "so that everything will dance when I play". So
the shepherd returned to his fire and played the clarinet.
Everything started to dance, the trees and the mountains. Then he
became hungry, and he went back to the Panagia and asked for
some meat. She told him that he would find some in his bag, and
there on his return he found the meat. After he had eaten he came
down to the mill at Davlia', and here Loukas began to embroider
the tale for my benefit, 'where there was a priest pasturing some
pigs, and he started playing the clarinet once again. The priest and
the pigs began to dance, and the priest danced so much that he fell
into a blackberry bush — the one where you found some blackberries — and the brambles caught his hair and his beard so that he
couldn't get out, and so he died.'

Loukas finished his absurd story and joined the rest of us in
laughter. The tale had little obvious moral and I wondered at the
odd association of the Panagia with the clarinet. Then I came across
another account suggesting a possible link with the pagan god
Pan.† In that case a priest had a good son who was a goatherd, to

†Recorded by J C Lawson, *Modern Greek Folk-Lore and Ancient Greek Religion*, p. 77

whom one day 'Panos' gave a kid with a skin of gold. The young man offered it as a burnt offering to God and in answer an angel promised him whatever he wished. The goatherd chose a magic pipe which would make everything dance that heard it and would therefore keep him safe from his enemies. When the king sent for the goatherd and threw him into prison, he played on his flute and made the houses and the rocks dance until they fell and crushed everything except him and his. The tale ends by suggesting that it had all been arranged by Panos to cleanse the world of evil.

It is difficult not to see in this earlier version a memory of Pan and his gift of music to the shepherd Daphnis. Many of the elements of the story of Panos are then found in Loukas' tale: the pastoral scene, the burnt offering, the angel, the pipe and the dancing, though the victim is no longer the king but the priest. Panos has become by happy alliteration the Panagia (who replaced both God and Panos), but it is an entirely natural alteration since Panos or Pan, the Great All, has become the All-Holy Panagia.

It is not merely the preservation of this pagan element in the popular imagination which is of interest but the underlying requirement by Greeks even today to see their gods in a living landscape around them. To bring it back a little way towards Osios Loukas from where we digressed, we can see within the panoply of saints of the Orthodox Church the Christian equivalents of many of the pagan gods, such as St Dionysios and St Demetrios, who answer a frankly polytheistic inclination which no amount of ecclesiastical justification can hide.

*

The Neoplatonist doctrine as developed by John of Damascus had an important impact on Byzantine art beyond that of once again allowing the representation of religious figures. In effect the artist became the interpreter of the divine. It was an art concerned principally not with the representation of human form but with religious, specifically Christian, spirituality; it sought not so much to show the external but to reveal the internal, to portray not bodily but spiritual beauty. Just as classical Greek art idealised the physical forms of their heroes and particularly the dead, so Byzantine artists idealised the great men of religion — but in an entirely different spirit. The thin ascetic replaced the well-proportioned body of classical art, and the idealisation moved from the plane of the physical to the realm of the divine. Byzantine art remained the heir to the classical-Hellenistic tradition, and Constantinople was itself a museum of antiquity and hence a source of periodic classical revivals, but the tradition remained entirely subordinate to the overall Christian purpose. Style and form changed from time to time during the long course of the Byzantine empire. The pendulum swung between the more lively, realistic art of the ancient tradition displayed in the mosaics at Daphni and the more formal, unyielding and monkish style so prominent at Osios Loukas, but under the patronage of a Christian emperor both strands remained the servile instruments of a religious scheme, an immutable Holy Order of saints and prophets beneath the countenance of Christ and the Panagia, whose holiness or divinity we might glimpse through the medium of their sacred images.

Mosaics, again a Hellenistic legacy, were particularly well suited to this grand purpose, since the light reflected by the small cubes of coloured glass or marble gave a movement and life to this concourse of largely static figures. The technique of mosaic art employed by Byzantine artists is still uncertain, but clearly the decoration of a large church took many years, possibly generations, to complete. If the majority of the mosaics at Osios Loukas are in the austere, monkish tradition thereby reflecting the taste of the Emperor Basil II who commissioned them, within the same church there are others in a freer style, perhaps the result of the work being carried on at a different period under the patronage of a different emperor, for example Constantine Monomachos, who was also responsible for the mosaics at Nea Moni.

A good example of the austere among the mosaics is to be found in the figure of St Luke on the south wall of the north transept. He has been placed opposite the important figures of Christ and the Mother of God. The saint, dressed in dark-blue mantle and black cap, is shown facing the spectator with hands uplifted in prayer. His pale cheeks are hollow and the unsmiling aspect of his face is emphasised in the lines of his long beard. The impact of the portrait comes partly from the simplicity and directness of the composition, especially the frontality of the figure, but also from the technique contrasting the dark body of the saint with the lighter tones of his head and arms; in addition the hands are unnaturally small so that the viewer is constantly made to return towards the face of the saint. His features show little expression and from his pallid brows

Mosaic of Saint Luke of Stiris

the eyes look inward towards another world which we do not know. This paragon of asceticism is not a very sympathetic figure — there is little of the human in the portrait — and yet that is a measure of the artist's success.

The position of the saint in the north transept is not fortuitous. The north transept was the point of junction with the church of the Panagia, and access could here be gained from the exo-narthex of that church to the Katholicon and vice-versa. It was therefore a convenient place for the shrine containing the relics of the saint, since visitors might approach it from either building. The mosaic portrait of St Luke almost faces the small recess where a shrine of black marble possessed his last earthly remains. The shrine is now empty. The saint's body was reputed to have miraculous properties, and the Franks of the Fourth Crusade are said to have stolen it away to Rome. However the saint has not altogether left Greece, since part of his skull is still to be found at the monastery of Philotheou on Mount Athos.

Some of the mosaics in the narthex, if at no point they approach those at the monastery of Daphni in respect of elegant archaism, nonetheless are executed in a somewhat freer, more natural style which is a little closer to the classical-Hellenistic tradition. They show an interest in harmonious composition, of both individual and groups of figures, and in the arrangement of their drapery, which has much in common with the cycle at Daphni and distinguishes them from the more severe style obvious in the interior of Osios Loukas. Here too there is a degree of individual characterisation and of expressiveness all the more effective for the strict limits within which it is allowed.

*

The church of the Panagia has little of the richness of the Katholicon. It has suffered worse from the passage of time and never possessed mosaics. Like Osios Loukas it is cruciform but the smaller dome here rests on a circular drum supported by arches, which are carried by four granite pillars with fine Corinthian capitals. At one time it was decorated with frescoes and some still remain in the side-chapel to the south of the sanctuary. Its chief ornament remains the marble floor which is a fine example of the mosaic design of geometric figures known as Opus Alexandrinum.

The crypt of Ayia Varvara, which is reached from the southern

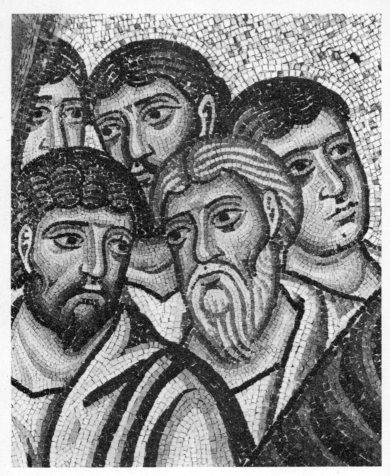

Detail from the mosaic of the Washing of the Feet of the Apostles

side of the Katholicon, still has its wall-paintings almost complete. Built as part of the foundations of the church above it, the crypt was also decorated in the eleventh century, although here frescoes were employed. The scheme of the paintings resembles that of the narthex, with medallions of the saints on the vaulted ceilings and scenes from the New Testament around the walls, and with the addition near the so-called tomb of St Luke of a representation of the Koimisis. The decoration of the areas of the ceiling between the medallions is similar to the painted decoration in the vaults on either side of the vestibule above, and the scenes on the walls even if crude in their execution and less reserved in expression have some of the spirit of those in the narthex.

The tomb alleged to be that of St Luke only dates from early this century, but the other two tombs (which are empty also) are much older. These consist of slabbed sarcophagi covered with marble lids, and by tradition they belong to the Emperor Romanos II and his wife. Unhappily we know that the Emperor (who anyway long predeceased the building) was buried far away in the church of the Holy Apostles in Constantinople. That church was later desecrated by the Franks and converted into a stable. After the recapture of Constantinople from the Franks in 1261 the embalmed body of Romanos II was found by two Greek officers. In one hand the dead Emperor was holding a shepherd's pipe. History does not tell us the last resting place of the Emperor with or without his pipe, but the two tombs in the crypt of St Luke probably once held the more prosaic remains of two of the early abbotts of the monastery.

7

ARACHOVA TOU PARNASSOU

Pausanias warns us that from the Megas crossroads where Laius was buried, the road to Delphi becomes steep and more difficult. Even with animals it might have taken as long as four hours to travel the twenty-four kilometres to the oracle since the first part of the journey, as far as modern-day Arachova, is uphill all the way. Whereas the new road runs high on the side of Cirphis, the former route stayed at the bottom of the defile between the mountains which is known as the Zemeno. About halfway up the Zemeno you can still see two short sections of the old Turkish highway. The road continued past the famous khan where in 1821 Vasilis Bousgos shed the first Turkish blood in Roumelia. The old buildings remain but are used now as a shepherd's madri, and a new khan has been built near a spring at the top of the Zemeno, among the Alpine meadows which here lie between Cirphis and Parnassos.

Shortly after the new Khan of the Zemeno we reach the watershed where the Pleistos torrent coming down from Parnassos flows into a great valley which falls away to the left; the stream then continues through the olive groves below Delphi towards the Bay of Itea. A road formerly descended into this valley beside the bed of the Pleistos towards Salona (Amphissa), and some travellers in the past used this method of approach to Delphi itself, although it meant a tiring ascent from the bed of the Pleistos up to the sanctuary. However there can be little doubt that the usual way to proceed towards Delphi has at all times been to remain high on the side of Parnassos, in the approximate line of the modern road.

Just beyond the bridge over the Pleistos ravine the country opens out on the right of the road and lies back against a row of huge limestone crags forming a continuous wall of rock. Near the east of this line a cleft called the Mana runs back into the rocks and brings the waters of the Pleistos down the mountainside. Much of this water has now been piped to Arachova, which accounts for the winter stream being nowadays something less than 'full and foaming', as Byron described it. Westwards from the Mana are the heights of Petritis and then Vlacholacca which lies above Arachova.

We can probably identify Vlacholacca with ancient Katopterius, the Lookout Place, from which Apollo was said to have shot the serpent at Delphi.

The first sight of Arachova is dramatic. You emerge from a short tunnel and turning a corner you suddenly see the village with its red-tiled roofs rising in terraces up the hillside opposite. In the middle a clocktower sits prominently on an isolated crop of rock, and at the top there is the large parish church of Ayios Georgios watching over the houses below. The main road to Delphi then passes through the centre of the village, where squeezed between unforgiving walls it is scarcely wide enough for two vehicles. The stream of traffic is continuous, and yet the Arachovites pay little attention as they stroll nonchalantly along the road or sit in the kafeneions under the Judas trees in the small plateia, oblivious of the world's restless desire to rush about. Some tourists do stop, enough to encourage many of the usual shops, and sometimes visitors fill a table at one of the restaurants along the main street. There are even a couple of hotels and a Xenia. But although Arachova is subjected to tourism it remains relatively unaffected by it. The tide simply flows past and the Arachovites are indifferent.

Most of the village is well away from the road. The handsome

Turkish road in the Zemeno

houses of stone, many with ironwork balconies and graceful arched doorways, have been built to withstand the severe winters that are inflicted upon Arachova owing to its proximity to Parnassos. They are hidden away in the narrow stepped lanes and many have withdrawn into their own internal courtyards as secret and secure as small fortresses.

Little is known of the predecessors of Arachova, and the first historical record is as late as 1435 when it was described by Cyriacus of Ancona as being well populated. However there was probably always a settlement in this fine position dominating the pass from central to western Greece, where it could exploit the rich slopes and uplands of Parnassos. At the end of the nineteenth century Frazer found a prosperous community of over three thousand inhabitants and despite the general drift in Greece from the villages to the cities the population is almost the same today. As the only substantial village on the south of Parnassos Arachova possesses the whole of that part of the mountain (in the sense that its inhabitants farm or graze it) as well as the valley below it. Its shepherds roam from the base of the Zemeno to Liacoura itself, and the farming land includes in addition to the rich wine-producing slopes around the village the beautiful upland plain of Livadi. Much of the milk from the huge herds of sheep and goats is made into cheese, and the feta (which may be made from either animal) is here particularly good. More evident in the shops than feta (and to my taste less good) is the attractive looking fromaella, a harder cheese not unlike kasseri, moulded into shape in baskets. Most eye-catching of all is another product of the sheep, the colourful woollen rugs hung outside the shops or draped over the balconies of the houses. These have usually been hand-woven in the traditional way on the looms which most homes in Arachova still possess, and are of very good quality.

Then there is the 'black' wine produced in the many vineyards around the village. It is entirely unresinated which should please those who have not yet acquired a liking for that delectable liquor, the 'vinum resinatum' of the ancients, and it is also without any of the chemicals now added to most retsinas to make them last. The flavouring of the Greek white wines with resin tapped from pine trees is not to everybody's taste, particularly on first acquaintance. Dodwell even asserted that 'the sour beer of England is preferable to the resinous beverage of Greece', but the taste once acquired is irresistible. At any rate the Greeks have found it so, and, whether or not the use of resin in wines originated from the habit of caulking the barrels with this glutinous substance, the Greeks have been deliberately giving this taste to many of their wines since the times of Pliny and Plutarch. Yet the practice has never been followed outside Greece, and even to drink retsina elsewhere seems inappropriate, whereas in its natural home, in the words of Patrick Leigh Fermor, 'it seems to have an alliance with the air in the promotion of well-being'. In Arachova, however, the black wine is suitable enough — even if less healthy and more costly than the black water of Parnassos that pours constantly from the village fountains.

Of the two principal churches the Metropolitan church of the Panagia, reached by some steps below the clocktower, has little interest. The other large church is that of Ayios Georgios already mentioned, which is approached from the central plateia by the long flight of steps near the fountain. Ayios Georgios is of some significance through its connection with the famous battle in November 1826 and with the hero of the battle, Georgios Karaskakis.

*

Georgios Karaskakis was a native of Agrapha and he followed a career similar to that of Odysseus Androutsos, having served Ali Pasha of Ioannina and then become a klepht and armatolos. His portrait shows a gipsy-looking figure with small features, a large moustache and long dark hair, wearing Turkish dress with a dagger and pistols thrust into his belt. Like Androutsos, Karaskakis was not altogether able to escape his background.

In the early years of the revolution Karaskakis' actions were less influenced by patriotism than by ambition, and his action as one of the Roumeliot chiefs during the seige of Mesolongi was frankly discreditable. For after the death of Byron he engaged himself more in rivalry with the other Greek leaders than in action against the Turks, and during the last heroic exit from Mesolongi before its fall in April 1826 (when he was outside the town) he gave almost no assistance. Yet in those dark days in summer 1826 when Reshid, the Turkish Serasker, succeeded in regaining control over almost all Roumelia including Salona and Levadia and was then able to commence the seige of Athens itself, Karaskakis did not follow some Greek captains in submitting to the Sultan's authority but chose to continue the struggle, even if with some thought of his own advancement. His association with Kolettes, who was dependent on the support of the Roumeliot military faction for his position in the government at Navplia, secured for Karaskakis the command of the Greek forces north of the isthmus, and thereafter his actions against the Turks if not always successful or even prudent were energetic and noted for his own personal daring.

When the Greek forces had failed to lift the siege of the Acropolis by Reshid, Karaskakis in command of some three thousand Greek troops moved north to Boeotia in the autumn of 1826 to harry the Turkish lines of communication and supply. In mid-November an expedition of Olympian armatoli under Kolettes landed near Atalanta to cause further disruption in Reshid's rear but this was defeated by the Turks under Mousta Bey who advanced from Levadia. Shortly afterwards the Turkish force, by now consisting of some two thousand men, mostly Albanians, under four Beys, began to move westwards to secure Salona (which was then under siege by Panourias). By this time Karaskakis was at Distomo, and late one night he there learnt the Turkish plans from a monk who had just arrived from the monastery of Jerusalem. The Turks were quartered at the monastery and their discussions had been overheard by one of the monks. The next morning, Karaskakis was told, they intended to send a small force over Parnassos to seize Arachova and so secure the pass to Salona until the remaining force arrived by the Zemeno. The Greek commander acted with considerable acumen and he at once despatched five hundred men to take up positions in the houses around Ayios Georgios. As a result the next morning the advance guard of Albanians was successfully repulsed from the village. When the remaining Turkish force had advanced up the Zemeno they too were unable to establish themselves in Arachova and the Turks were forced to make camp in an exposed position on the hillside above Ayios Georgios. Karaskakis advanced from Distomo with the rest of the Greeks and establishing himself in the courtyard of the church proceeded to blockade the Turks in their camp by encircling them. The Greeks also acted to prevent any help reaching the enemy by securing the road to the east at the Megas crossroads and to the west at Delphi.

The weather quickly turned from a mild autumn to severe winter, with heavy falls of snow, and the position of the Turks — under fire from all sides and without tents or adequate supplies, their terms of capitulation rejected — became desperate. On the fifth day the commander of the Albanians Mousta Bey received a fatal wound from a bullet, and on the seventh day, 24 November by the old calendar, after a night when the snow had almost buried the besieged alive, a body of Albanians having learnt of the death of their commander began a disorderly exit from the camp; during the afternoon they broke out in the direction of the Mana and the monastery of Jerusalem, and soon they were being followed by the rest of the Turkish camp. The Greeks, many of whom were sheltering in the houses, were slow to respond but under the encouragement of Karaskakis himself some rushed the former Turkish position while others pursued the fugitives through the snow.

The Turks and Albanians, weakened by cold and hunger, and unfamiliar with the ground, were mostly overtaken by the Greeks and easily cut down with cutlass and knife. So soundless was the slaughter to the ears of Karaskakis at Ayios Georgios that he feared the enemy was succeeding in escaping and he offered rewards to those who would bring back the heads of any of the fugitives. There was little need. About thirteen hundred Turks and Albanians were killed with little or no resistance. Of the rest many died on the mountain and a small number managed to escape over Parnassos, suffering cruelly from frostbite and exposure. The slaughter lasted until dusk. The Greeks then returned to Arachova carrying the heads of the dead and so duly received their rewards from Karaskakis outside the church of St George.

The celebration of the Greek success began as the manhunt was still continuing. The Greek leader gave thanks in the church and as the young men went after the Turks the old men danced. Then as the heads of the enemy were brought in they were piled into two large heaps in the small Plateia Trophaiou (the Square of the Trophy) as it has become known, just below the church. On top of one pile was placed the head of Mousta Bey and on the other than of Kehaya Bey, one of Reshid's own officers. The Greeks were doing no more than following the barbaric Ottoman practice of making a pyramidical trophy of the heads of the vanquished. Nearby the words were posted, 'A Trophy of the Greeks from the barbarian Ottomans raised up on 24 November 1826 in Arachova'.† A song from that time recalls how

---

†A bust of Karaskakis with the same inscription now stands on the left-hand side of the road at the entrance of the town from Delphi.

'They built a tower, there at the Platania,
And the tower was huge, high as a cypress tree,
And around it danced the pallikaria.'

The news of the successful outcome of Arachova fired the Greeks who for some time had known nothing but failure. A service of thanksgiving took place at Aegina (the new seat of government) and a eulogy was delivered by the statesman Trikoupis, while Karaskakis despatched to the capital the heads of the four beys together with an offical delegation carrying his report. 'The darkness of Mesolongi has lifted, the horizon is once again bright', the government newspaper wrote, and for a time the good fortune continued. Karaskakis successfully operated against Turkish convoys, and much of central Greece was recovered including Salona. In February 1827 he achieved a notable victory at Distomo following which the Turks were forced to retire to Euboea, and he then marched south to cooperate in an attack on Reshid's army besieging the Acropolis. However tragedy soon struck. Before the attack could be made on Reshid, the Greek commander was fatally wounded in a skirmish and he died the following day, 23 April, on the festival of St George. Finlay with his customary cynicism observed that Karaskakis 'fell at a moment favourable to his reputation. He had not always acted as a patriot but his recent success in Phocis contrasted with [other] defeats [of European commanders] in a manner so flattering to national vanity that his name was idolised by the irregular troops'.† In fact despite his earlier depredations of the Greek population the former armatolos died leaving no property to his heir except his sword, having spent all his wealth on the war. For the last year of his life at least the pursuit of his own personal ambitions became identical with the success of Greek arms.

After the death of Karaskakis the Greek forces under the command of Cochrane suffered total disaster at Phaleron, and the Acropolis was finally forced to surrender to the Turks in June 1827. Once again the Greeks were in a desperate situation. Although many of them were still under arms Reshid was free to reimpose Turkish control over Roumelia, while in the Morea Ibrahim Pasha who had devastated the country in the previous year and was now at Navarino with the Egyptian fleet could resume his operations

†*History of Greece*, Vol. vi, p. 429

with little to stop him. Throughout Greece the population was starving. Nothing was likely to save the Greeks from falling completely under Turkish dominion once again except for the intervention of the three Great Powers — Britain, France and Russia — for whom the Greek cause had been throughout a matter of almost total indifference if not opposition. At last in July 1827, after Britain and Russia saw common cause in the pacification of the East, the three powers proposed an enforced armistice to end hostilities. This the Turks rejected and the Greeks while accepting it in principle disregarded it in practice. At the end of September Captain Hastings, one of the most gallant of the Philhellenes, steamed into the Corinthian Gulf with his steamship the Karteria and a small naval force and destroyed a Turkish squadron which was anchored at the Scala, the port of Salona (near modern Itea). With this and other Greek ventures continuing there was little hope of Ibrahim remaining inactive in Navarino unless the Allied fleet (of British, French and Russian ships) continued a blockade indefinitely; moreover the Turkish army was already operating in the interior. On 20 October the Allied admirals entered the bay of Navarino 'to renew proposals' — in effect to force Ibrahim to leave the Morea. When firing began (started by the Turks), most of the Ottoman fleet was destroyed.

The battle of Navarino was not quite the end of the matter. Ibrahim did not evacuate the Morea until almost a year later, and continental Greece was not abandoned until 1829, when war with Russia finally forced this upon the Sultan. But the intervention of the Allies at Navarino signalled the beginning of the end for the Turks in Greece, and it is the irony of the revolution that the war was not won by the military exploits of the Greeks, still less the Philhellenes, however much both may have contributed to keeping the cause alive, but by the last-minute intervention of the European powers in their own separate interests. The significance of Navarino was not lost upon the Greeks. Gordon who lived through those times wrote in his *History of the Greek Revolution* published a few years later, 'Those only who have through a providential interposition escaped the pressure of some fearful calamity can conceive the exultation excited in Greece by the event of Navarin; the people were mad with joy, and crowded the churches to vent the overflowings of national gratitude...'† When

†*History of the Greek Revolution*, Vol. II, p.438

the news was received in the Gulf of Corinth the guns of the Karteria saluted the victory. In the villages the church bells rang and on Parnassos huge fires were lit. It did indeed seem like a deliverance.

*

We have not moved so far as it may appear from Arachova. For it was not long before these stirring events came to be celebrated in a festival which has continued to this day. 'Panigiraki ginetai psila ston Ai Georgi', the famous song goes — a Carnival goes on high up at Ayios Georgios. Significantly the celebrations do not take place on the anniversary of the battle of Arachova (in November) but over the feast of St George which is on 23 April. (If however St George's Day falls in Lent, the festival is held immediately after Easter.) In fact the Panigiraki recalls more than just what occurred at Arachova.

It may be remembered that Georgios Karaskakis had died on his name-day, 23 April 1827, about six months before Navarino. As the battle of Arachova had taken place in the area of the church of Ayios Georgios, who was already regarded as the protector of Arachova, the celebration of the victory on the occasion of the saint's festival on 23 April had the further advantage of also remembering the hero of the battle who had died on that very day. Within a few years of the end of the war the festival included a race, probably for the former pallikaria, for which the prizes were lambs dedicated to the saint by the shepherds of Arachova. Also after the service in Ayios Georgios the old men danced in the courtyard of the church as they sang the song *Panigiraki*. It is not difficult to see in these two events memories of the final charge of the Greek forces to the camp of Mousta Bey on the hillside above the church and then the dance of the old men later that evening after the service of thanksgiving to St George.

The festival now spreads over four days and it is well known throughout the region. On the second day some of the men of Arachova, dressed in tunics and foustanellas, race up the hill of Mousta Bey to the former position of the Turkish camp, contesting the prize of a lamb. On the previous evening, once the church service is over, they have danced the Panigiraki. The song itself is heavy with symbolism:

'A battle goes on high up at Ayios Georgios,

The war was great and the country was small;
The Turkish dragon yet holds the freedom for which the
    Greeks have thirsted,
The Christians and the Klephts...
Three Women came together to go and tell the dragon —
Dragon, leave the water for the Greeks to drink.'

This is where we see that more than the local success at the battle of Arachova is involved in the celebrations. The three women were the three Great Powers who at last confronted the Turks in 1827, and the song while remembering Arachova is in reality more of a celebration of the battle of Navarino and the part played by the European powers in forcing the Turks out of Greece. The song originated at a time when the Turkish dragon had finally slunk away and the Greeks of Arachova were able to celebrate not only their success but also their freedom.

At a later time the tradition inevitably arose that St George himself had appeared in the battle of Arachova, leading the slaughter of the Turks from his horse. This embellishment was bound to find its way into the verses of the Panigiraki and the song was later lengthened to include the slaying of the 'dragon' by the saint. And what was the occasion for St George's intervention? Why, of course, to protect the three presumptuous young women from the dragon!

*

Of the church of Ayios Georgios only the belfry predates the revolution, the main edifice having been rebuilt in 1875. In a small garden to one side of the courtyard there is another bust of Karaskakis (who is also shown on a bronze plaque attacking the Turks), but in addition there is an old cannon captured from the Turks in 1826. The saint has not even been able to leave this relic alone. The story is told that when during the last war the Italians were in occupation of the village they seized the gun in case it be used against them; it had been left on the field of battle by Karaskakis and its only use had been to signal feast days and other important events. However the horses would pull the cannon no further than the church and nothing would induce them to move. At this stage the sergeant commanding the operation is said to have seen a vision of St George. Then an attempt was made to destroy the weapon with explosives, but they only succeeded in blowing off the end of the barrel. Finally the Italians decided it was best to leave the cannon where it was, and there it remains today.

*

'Arachova tou Parnassou'. Arachova belongs to Parnassos, as much as Parnassos belong to Arachova. The character of the village, the occupations of the villagers and above all the climate are all directly affected by the mountain, which dominates the entire surrounding region. The main summit, known as Liacoura, is barely 2400 metres high, which is lower than Olympos and even neighbouring Giona. Yet 'in the wild pomp of mountain majesty' (in the words of Byron) Parnassos is not matched by peaks many times its size.

'High is the fir, and higher still Giona,/But they bow down and yield to old Liacoura', goes the demotic song. On every side the mountain presents a different face. To the west the long ridge of Gerontovrachos has the appearance of a sleeping figure; to the south we see a crenellated wall of bare limestone crags; and to the east and around to the north the spurs rise from the valleys of Boeotia and the Cephisos in dark fir-clad slopes that gather up to a line of peaks lorded by Liacoura itself.

In the winter snow lies uniformly over the upper areas, occasionally descending on Arachova and the other villages on the lower slopes, and a chilling wind then blows off the mountain. In early summer, as the snow melts in the warmer air, the moisture encourages in the upland valleys a covering of wild flowers and pasture which lasts almost until the autumn, when the rain leaves once again a scattering of snow on the highest points. Then the shepherds who have spent the summer grazing their animals below the summits drive them down the mountain to find safer quarters before the full onset of winter.

Although less fertile in general than Helicon one area of Parnassos has been extensively cultivated in the past, namely the beautiful plain of Livadi above Arachova. This is reached by the road for Eptalophos and Amphiclia which leaves Arachova near the bust of Karaskakis (on the main road) and rises up through the vineyards above the village, with dramatic views over the Pleistos gorge, until it reaches the shoulder on the edge

Uplands of Parnassos

of the upland plateau. Below as you look down on the plain the fields stretch far away to the edges of the wooded heights that surround them, while high above you see the gaunt flank of Gerontovrachos, Old Man Rock, the next summit to Liacoura. In May the fields are thick with flowers, a carpet of white and blue, repeating the springtime miracle of a month earlier on the coast. In the middle of the plain there is a small cluster of buildings known as Kalivia belonging to those Arachovites with land on Livadi and traditionally used in the summer during the periods of sowing and harvesting.

The plain of Livadi was formerly the starting point for most of those setting out to climb Parnassos and from Kalivia it is five or six hours walk to the top of Liacoura. There are other ways too: from Davlia via the monastery of Jerusalem (about eight hours), and a more direct route from Arachova by a steep path up Vlacholacca. However from the direction of Livadi the approach has now been made easier for those with cars by the new roads created in recent years to reach the two areas on the higher slopes where winter skiing has been developed. (By all accounts the skiing is very good, particularly at the Ski Centre — the

Chionodromikon Kentron — situated on the north side of the mountain.) To reach these areas from Kalivia you follow the road towards Eptalophos as it continues across the plain. After 2 kilometres, near a bridge, there is a turning to the left onto a dirt track for the Corycian Cave. A further couple of kilometres brings you to a road on the right which leads off in the direction of the Ski Centre and the Athens Ski Club. This road winds up through the trees and eventually divides, left to Phterolacca (also reached from Amphiclia) and thence to the Ski Centre, and right to the Athens Ski Club which is situated high on the west flank of Gerontovrachos just above the tree line.

The Ski Club is not far from the Refuge of Sarandari belonging to the Greek Alpine Club, and on the slope above the Club near the ski lift red marks may be seen painted on the rocks pointing the way to the summit. By following the red markers it takes two and a half to three hours' difficult walk to reach the summit. The other way to Liacoura, namely to walk from the Ski Centre, is much easier and takes a little less time, although the sense of achievement is thereby correspondingly reduced, since a dirt road continues above the Centre all the way to the area which lies immediately below the summits. I have gone both ways to the top, and on both occasions have missed one of the principal objects of the exercise — the magnificent view over much of the map of Greece. Daybreak in the last part of August is said to be the best time, whereas a July dawn and an October noon appear to be among the worst, with cloud or haze limiting the horizon to little more than the other peaks of the mountain.

When the weather is clear you can obtain from the summit the most extensive view in Greece, from the north of Thessaly to Arcadia and from the entrance to the Corinthian Gulf to the furthest part of Attica. This is how Edward Clarke described his experience on a December day in 1801 when, undeterred by the snow, he arrived on the top of Liacoura: 'Having been for years engaged in visiting the tops of mountains, the author must still confess that he never saw anything to compare with the view which be beheld from the summit of Parnassos...The Gulf of Corinth had long looked like an ordinary lake; and it was now reduced to a pond. Towards the north beyond all the plains of Thessaly appeared Olympus with its many tops clad in shining snow and expanding its vast breadth distinctly to the view. The other mountains of Greece, like the surface of the ocean in a rolling calm, rose in vast heaps according to their different altitudes; but the eye ranged over every one of them...We looked down upon Achaia, Argolis, Elis and Arcadia as upon a model.'† The traveller's enthusiasm was not in the least dampened by some small part of the horizon being obscured by cloud — it was after all the middle of winter.

†*Travels*, p.260

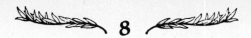

8

AROUND PARNASSOS

Between Arachova and Delphi the modern road follows the same general line as the ancient way as it traverses the side of the Pleistos valley. There is little pleasure in walking along the asphalt, and arrival at Delphi from this direction by conventional transport is anyway spectacular enough. There is though another approach to the sanctuary of Apollo which can be made on foot, by perhaps the most dramatic and certainly the oldest remaining route, namely by the Kake Skala. The Kake Skala descends the cliffs above the sanctuary and despite its name (which means something like the Bad Steps) it is easy enough. However to reach the top of the Skala takes some time. From Arachova you must first walk up to Livadi by the road to Eptalophos and Amphiclia, and there (most simply) proceed via the Corycian Cave, a good trek of some four hours or so but well worth it. The way to the Cave (and beyond) is described later in this chapter.

Livadi can of course also be reached from Eptalophos to the north, and to arrive there from that side I propose to retrace the steps of a journey by foot around Parnassos from the east. This route lies mostly away from motor roads and includes several interesting places. It takes a number of days to complete.

The village of Davlia to which we diverged in Chapter Five from the road to Delphi will serve as our point of departure, and initially we shall follow the valley of the Cephisos northwards towards its source. Pausanias observed long ago that 'the land beside the Cephisos is distinctly the best in Phocis for planting and sowing and pasture', and the fertility of the valley has been one of the constant factors in the social development of central Greece, having encouraged settlements along its length from the Stone Age to the present day. The villages and cities have mostly stood away from the river on the lower slopes of Kallidromon and Parnassos, and by walking along the side of the latter we can visit several of these historic places without approaching the modern road in the middle of the valley.

The first is Ayia Marina, a small tobacco-producing village situated beside the bed of a winter stream. From Davlia you can reach Ayia Marina through the beautiful defile, the Steno, that also leads to Parorio, but the higher route is quicker. Starting from the church of Ayios Elias in the upper part of Davlia you walk out of the village roughly northwards and cross a small valley before making up to the left towards the wide fold in the land directly below Parnassos. Here a broad path runs most of the way to Ayia Marina, and the bells of the animals grazing in the pournari keep you company. After about one and a half hours the path arrives at the chapel of Saint Marina by a large plane tree above a pipe of good water, and from here it is only a short step to the plateia and the kafeneion in the centre of the village.

I was told about the saint who had given her name to the village as I sat late one afternoon in the small square shading my eyes against the sun as it sank low over Liacoura. The story is simple enough. Years ago there was a devilish figure, horned and black-skinned, called Cholera which lived by the spring in the place where the chapel was later built. This terrible creature brought disease and caused most of the villagers to die. Then at last a local woman called Marina succeeded in catching hold of the devil and she cut off its head near a rock that can still be seen. Marina was made a saint and a chapel was built in her honour. That at least is the popular account, and those to whom I talked believed it quite literally without any apparent recognition of the actual event at the centre of the myth, which was obviously a serious outbreak of disease that had providentially just failed to carry off the whole population. The church has done little as usual to alter matters. The priest just smiles and shrugs his shoulders, as if he faintly disapproves of such naive beliefs and yet is resigned to do nothing to change them. The chapel itself, which is said by some to date from the seventh century, has several icons of Ayia Marina. Most depict the saint grasping the devil by the hair with one hand and wielding the cross in the other. However the artist of one is bolder and as in the story has decided upon the knife as a better weapon than the cross. And so it was.

The village square has been recently renamed after Philomelos, the Phocian general from Ledon, who was responsible for seizing Delphi in the fourth century BC and who was later forced to hurl himself from a precipice after being defeated at Neon. We do not know for certain where Ledon was, but it can probably be placed at Ayia Marina where on a plateau above a rocky outcrop to the southwest of the village there are the ruins of an ancient city. I stumbled over the place, without knowing of its existence, one damp November day when walking from Davlia I had strayed from the path. It came as a surprise to find looming out of the mist the angle of a tower, some ten courses high. On either side of the tower walling stands in places to four or five courses, about 2.5 metres high. This then was part of the acropolis. The rest of the city lay on the lower ground before it, where the foundations of many buildings are still visible. Ledon was destroyed by Philip after the Phocian War, rightly so according to Pausanias who says its destruction was as richly deserved as the ruin of Paris' Troy. If these are indeed the remains of Ledon, the walls were rebuilt and the city was finally abandoned at a much later date.

Philomelos met his death at Neon, and that ancient city was almost certainly situated at Tithorea, the next village to the north. When on that same November day I walked out of Ayia Marina in the direction of Tithorea, I was accompanied by a former proedros (mayor) who kindly insisted on showing me the first part of the way, though it is obvious enough. As we walked he told me how during the civil war as proedros he had been a target of attack for the communists and at times had been forced to sleep out among the bushes beside the path. In the gentle, rolling country that here falls down to the Cephisos it was more than usually difficult to imagine such times. Ahead of us we could now see the great green cliff above Tithorea, and after leaving my guide I arrived at the village in under an hour.

*

The effect of arriving at Tithorea was spectacular. By now the mist and cloud which had caused me to lose my way that morning above Ayia Marina had slightly lifted. Some patches of blue sky had emerged and the sun painted yellow flares on the hills across the valley. Yet the mist still hung directly on top of the cliffs above Tithorea and in preventing the eye from travelling up the great ravine behind the village made its situation more than usually mysterious. High among the trees a large tower was visible, daubed with whitewash, and from this I could just make out the line of a wall descending the wooded hillside in huge steps. Lower down was the village itself, caught between the base of the cliff and a last twist in the ravine as it here emerges from deep inside the mountain. The houses of Tithorea thus lay as if on a platform above the bed of its winter torrent, enthroned on a green cliff and crowned by cloud.

At the bottom of the village there is a bridge over the stream and from here it is a last tiring pull up the main road to the centre of the village. As you proceed you see ahead the substantial remains of the northern wall of the ancient city, hung now with ivy, and at the angle of the wall beside the road there is an ancient tower in almost perfect preservation. Beyond this tower the former west wall of the city runs alongside the road until finally it disappears among the houses. It is the upper part of this west wall which then re-emerges above the village and terminates a little above the whitewashed tower. The walls on the west and north therefore protected the city on its two exposed sides, while to the south and east it was safely fenced by the cliff and by the ravine. Even today the village occupies much the same position, and the honey-coloured walls of ancient Tithorea still contain most of the houses within their angle. Few of the ancient cities of Boeotia, Phocis and Locris compare with Tithorea in the romance of its setting, and its remaining fortifications rank among the finest in Greece.

The name of the city and the later village on this site has changed several times. In the period of classical antiquity it was known as Neon. Little is recorded about that city except that it was destroyed by Xerxes after the Phocians had fled to safety on top of the cliff

Fourth century BC masonry in the isodomic trapezoidal style in a tower at Tithorea

above (called Tithorea), and it was again ruined by Philip at the end of the Phocian War during the course of which the defeated Philomelos had killed himself by probably jumping into the ravine below the city. After its rebuilding at the time of the other Phocian cities following the battle of Chaironia, the city became known as Tithorea, a name it retained throughout the Roman empire. Then as so often we lose sight of the place until the Turkish period when we find it as Velitsa. The village has now been given the official name of Tithorea and that is what you will find on the maps. However it is still known locally by the old Turkish name, just as are Amphiclia (Dadi), Elatia (Drachmani) and many other places.

*

It is another circumstance connected with the War of Independence that detains the visitor at Tithorea. It was here that Odysseus Androutsos and his English ally, Edward Trelawny, made their base in a cave halfway up a cliff on the side of the ravine where it runs back behind the village, and there are few places better equipped to stir the imagination. To reach this cave is about an hour's walk from Velitsa. You must take the left-hand street from the plateia where the buses stop in the centre of the village and follow the road up to the restored church of the Panagia. Here, outside the church, on a terrace that looks up the ravine towards the distant summits of Parnassos you will see the bust of Androutsos, honoured I recall on one occasion with a large wreath of bay. The way out of the village beside the ravine is then obvious enough: you follow a narrow path, once guarded by an ancient fortification, between the cliff-face and a precipitous drop to the bed of the torrent. The path then continues towards a grove of oaks near the chapel of Ayios Georgios. A little further beyond the trees you will find a pipe in the rock discharging water into a hollowed tree trunk. If you then proceed a short distance in the direction of the ravine to the area of a circular stone-built madri and look away to the cliffs on the right you will see among several caves one which is about a third of the way up the face of the rock with a line of iron ladders reaching up to its mouth. That is the cave of Androutsos, the Mavre Tripa or Black Hole as it has been called, and it is a stiff walk across the rocky slope to the base of the ladders.

By struggling up the series of four metal ladders you gain with

some difficulty a terrace some 30 metres or more long lying under
the open sky a little below the mouth of the cave itself. Inside the
cave, originally reached by another short ladder, the floor slopes
upwards so that at its furthest point it meets the roof, while on
either side there are various galleries. As with many things that
have been eagerly anticipated the cave was smaller than I had

Trelawny's cave at Tithorea

imagined, yet after the exertion of climbing up to the cave I shall not easily forget the sight of the cloud swirling around the entrance and then, as it was slowly dispersed by the sun, the view over the entire Cephisos valley to the north and west.

Odysseus Androutsos we have come across before. As one of Ali Pasha's officers he had been in command of the passes between Levadia and Salona just before the War of Independence, but with the advance of the Turks he had escaped to the Ionian Islands. He later reappeared at the end of April 1821 after the capture of Levadia by Diakos, his former protopallikar, and adopting the role of a patriot hastened with a small force to reinforce Diakos and Bishop Isaias at Alamana, only to meet the already victorious Turkish army at Gravia. There his fierce defence, before he was finally forced to evacuate the khan, considerably enhanced his reputation. With Diakos dead Odysseus emerged as the most important captain in East Greece, and whether acting as the official commander of the Greek forces or as an independent chief (depending upon the current degree of organisation of the Greek authorities) he operated with varying success against the Turks in the first three years of the war. However Odysseus' patriotism went no further than the service of his own interests, and it was not long before his self-interest suggested to him a different and eventually fatal course. Throughout the years of the war until his death in 1825 Odysseus retained the mind and morality of a klepht and when his independent position in East Greece was threatened by the manoeuvres of the politicians of the central government — men like Mavrocordato and Kolettes — Odysseus retired to his mountain lair which he had taken the precaution of fortifying and provisioning, and from there attempted to dictate events by colluding with the Turks.

It was a short time before this that the fascinating figure of Edward Trelawny had entered onto the stage. In the company of Odysseus, Trelawny for a time was able to play in real life the role of a Byronic hero that he had already cast for himself in stories of his supposed adventures in the East Indies and the deserts of Arabia. After a brief and unsuccessful period in the Royal navy and then a disastrous marriage, at the age of twenty-six Trelawny as the younger son of a well-to-do family had been forced by his relatively small allowance to go and live abroad. At the beginning of 1822, drawn by the fame of Byron he arrived at Pisa where at that time the Shelleys were also living. There Trelawny had little to

offer by comparison with the wealth, the fame and literary
endeavours of the Pisa circle, and so he took refuge in stories of an
adventurous past such as might befit the hero of one of Byron's
own romantic poems, such as *The Corsair*, which had greatly
affected him when still an adolescent. In his fertile imagination he
assumed the character of a corsair or buccaneer, and although the
stories of the past did not deceive everyone, and certainly not
Byron, who later said that Trelawny could not tell the truth even to
save his life, he was an entertaining and striking companion. Mary
Shelley described him as 'a kind of half-Arab Englishman — whose
life has been as changeful as that of Anastasius and who recounts
the adventures of his youth as eloquently and well as the imagined
Greek...His company is delightful.' With his reputation as a sea-
dog (in fact he was only ever a midshipman), it was Trelawny who
designed Shelley's sailing boat the *Don Juan* which was modelled on
an American privateer and which was totally unseaworthy; it was
Trelawny who, after the poet had drowned on one of the *Don Juan's*
early voyages, had played the part of the man of action, supervising
the cremation of the poet's remains on the beach of Viarregio and
burning his hand as he snatched Shelley's heart from the flames;
and it was with Trelawny that Byron finally sailed for Greece in
July of the following year (1823), after Trelawny had (according to
him) strengthened the famous man's resolve to assist the war.

Byron's position was as the representative of the recently formed
Greek Committee, which had been established in London as a
means of channelling both money and manpower to the Greeks,
and he prudently decided to remain in the Ionian island of
Cephalonia, then under British jurisdiction, while he waited on
developments in Greece. There was faction among the Greek
leaders, and it was unclear to whom any money, whether it was the
English loan or Byron's personal funds, should best be directed.
Trelawny chafed at the delay and with another Philhellene
travelled to the Morea to see the situation for himself. Byron's last
words to Trelawny were, 'let me hear from you often — come back
soon. If things are farcical they will do for *Don Juan*; if heroical, you
shall have another canto of *Childe Harold'.*† Dressed as a Souliote,
with red Albanian jacket, baggy trousers and a turban, Trelawny as
Byron's agent busied himself between the Greek leaders. He was
more impressed by the chieftains like Kolokotronis than the

†Trelawny, *Records of Shelley, Byron and the Author* (1878), Vol. II, p. 119

politicians like Mavrocordato. At this time, in late 1823, Kolokotronis was chief of the Morea, Mavrocordato commanded in West Greece and Odysseus in the east. Trelawny counselled Byron to come to the mainland to attend a proposed conference of the Greek leaders at Salona, a proposal which became all the more important when in the Morea a civil was broke out between Kolokotronis and the nominal government. When however Byron did move to Greece it was to Mesolongi, in Mavrocodato's territory, and there he remained, subjected to the intrigues of those constantly applying to him for money, ineffective and yet by his mere presence an inspiration to the Greek cause.

Meanwhile Trelawny had met Odysseus in Athens, and joined him in an expedition to Euboea. In Odysseus Trelawny saw a real model of that kind of hero he had fashioned for himself in his fantasies. Indeed the former officer of Ali Pasha was capable of impressing other less romantic minds, like that of the Englishman Stanhope who wrote to Byron, 'Odysseus is a doing man: he governs with a strong arm and is the only man in Greece who can preserve order. He professes himself of no faction...Odysseus is most anxious to unite the interests of Eastern and Western Greece for which purpose he is desirous immediately of forming a congress at Salona'. The truth lay closer to Odysseus' own desire to ensure that his almost independent position would be preserved and that he too would be a beneficiary of the English loans when they arrived.

In April 1824 while Odysseus waited in Salona Trelawny set out for Mesolongi to implore Byron and Mavrocordato to attend the congress. As he was travelling he received the startling news of Byron's death. 'Thus by a stroke of fate my hopes of being of use in Greece were extinguished', he later wrote in his exaggerated manner. He nonetheless continued on to Mesolongi arriving a few days after the poet's death and in time to see Byron's embalmed body — 'more beautiful in death than in life'. His statement that at last he had unravelled the mystery of Byron's lameness, when he lifted the shroud and observed that 'both of his feet were clubbed and his legs withered at the knee', earned him a justifiable reputation for gross hyperbole after its publication in his *Recollections* in 1858.

This was not the end of Trelawny's activities in Greece, although little that he later did was of any usefulness. While the congress of Salona went ahead as a purely regional assembly, he succeeded (despite Mavrocordato's objections) in wresting from the defences of Mesolongi four brass field guns and a quantity of stores for Odysseus, and with these trophies he returned to the cave at Tithorea which the Greek had been using as his base of operations. The cavern was now converted into a fortified stronghold with the assistance of two Philhellenes including a Scottish artillery officer by the name of Thomas Fenton. Trelawny described it in this way: 'This cavern Odysseus had with great ingenuity managed to ascend, and convert into a place of safety for his family and effects during the war. The only access to it was by ladders bolted to the rock...(from the top ladder) you entered a vaulted guardroom, pierced with lancet-holes for musketry. This opened on a broad terrace, 25 metres in length, screened by a substantial parapet-wall, breast-high, with embrasures mounted with cannon.'† On the higher terraces within the cave there were small houses built of wood and sufficient stores of food and ammunition, so it was said, to keep a large force for twenty years. There was even spring water seeping from the rock. By removing the top ladder access was rendered impossible and the place impregnable, even apart from the men whom Odysseus stationed below the cave.

Odysseus had need of such precautions. His position in 1824 became increasingly isolated. In the two civil wars, which consumed such large amounts of the English loans and from which Kolettes emerged as the most powerful figure in Greece, Odysseus stood to one side sharing neither in defeat nor victory. He remained without allies, yet with enemies within the government who resented his independent command. He succeeded in obtaining no share in the first instalment of the English loan, and even his lieutenant Ghouras to whom he had entrusted the command of the Acropolis at Athens was wavering in his loyalty. After an apparent assassination attempt at Navplia Odysseus retired to Roumelia, in Gordon's description 'evidently a fallen man'.

Trelawny says he urged Odysseus to resign his command; sooner or later he would be called upon to defend the country when it had been left defenceless by the depredations of the politicians. Odysseus' reply was characteristic and it betrays a mentality appropriate to a period that was already passing. 'This part of the country, Livadia, my father inherited from his father, who won it by his valour, and when it was lost through the

†Ibid., p. 167

treachery of the Venetians, who sold my father to the Sultan, I regained it by my wits and have kept it by my sword.'† Despite the opposition of the Greek government Odysseus was determined to keep his territory. Acting in the old tradition the former klepht came to an accommodation with the Turks. At first this was limited to a three month's truce under the terms of which East Greece was to be neutral territory. During this period the Turks and Greeks co-existed uneasily, with the Ottoman cavalry on the plain and Odysseus' men above it on the hills. While the Greek played his dangerous game Trelawny remained in the cave.

Then finally in early 1825 Androutsos entered into an agreement with the Pasha of Negropont that gave him an armatolik in his old territories, a position such as he had held under Ali Pasha. He maintained to Trelawny that he was doing this solely to put pressure on the government to give him the necessary funds for the defence of East Greece from the threatened Turkish advance. However the reality which Trelawny did not like to admit was that his hero had turned traitor, and the Englishman allowed himself to be taken in by the Greek's specious explanations so that he became in the end the victim of his own romanticism. After the two men had conveyed Odysseus' accumulated treasure to hiding places at Thebes (as yet undiscovered), Odysseus formally entrusted the custody of the cave to Trelawny who in turn sealed his loyalty to the Greek by marrying his thirteen-year old half-sister Tersitsa in a ceremony in the cavern's tiny chapel. Trelawny relates his parting from Odysseus: 'As we sat on the turf by a broken fountain, he placed his rough hairy hand on my bosom, saying, "You have a strong heart in a strong body: you find fault with me for distrusting my countrymen — I never doubted you."'‡ Trelawny was soon to need all his strength of heart and body.

Odysseus, operating alongside Turkish forces, was now campaigning openly against Ghouras. In April he was surrounded by superior numbers near Atalanta and perhaps already regretting his espousal of the Turkish side chose to surrender, in the hope of receiving merciful treatment from his former lieutenant. For the time being Odysseus was imprisoned on the Acropolis while Ghouras, no doubt lured by its reputed treasures, bent every effort against the cave at Tithorea. On one occasion when Trelawny was

†Ibid., p. 166
‡Ibid., p. 183

Bust of Odysseus Androutsos at Tithorea

below the cavern he was stalked and shot at by the Greeks and only just regained the fortress. Then Ghouras tried deception, through the medium of a letter said to have been written by Odysseus asking the Englishman to hand over the cave, but Trelawny was not to be deceived. Finally half-measures were abandoned. On 17 June Odysseus was murdered; he was strangled and his body thrown from the Frankish tower on the Acropolis to give the appearance of his having fallen when trying to escape. At about the same time an assassination attempt within the cave was made against Trelawny by Fenton who had been persuaded or bribed by Mavrocordato. Fenton had suborned a young Englishman called Whitcombe to take aim at Trelawny while the three of them were shooting at targets on the terrace of the cave. Two balls hit Trelawny between the shoulders, but although grave the wounds were not fatal. Fenton was immediately killed by Trelawny's second-in-command, and Whitcombe would have been hanged had Trelawny not intervened. For several weeks Trelawny lay in the cave without bandages or medicine and barely able to move. When it became evident that he was going to survive and also that Whitcombe had merely been the creature of Fenton, the young man was released. This generous act was one of the few features of the whole story of the cave, apart from his remarkable survival, that can be placed to Trelawny's credit.

Trelawny's exit from Greece was considerably less dignified than he had hoped for, and although he had achieved fame — his exploits were by now common knowledge in England — it was not altogether of the nature he would have preferred. Through the intervention of two Englishmen, Major d'Arcy Bacon who had been travelling in Greece and Captain Hamilton an officer in the Royal Navy, both moved more by motives of humanity than sympathy, Mavrocordato was persuaded to allow Trelawny to leave Greece. Bacon together with some of Ghouras' men accompanied the wounded man and his bride to the Bay of Anticyra where a British ship embarked them for the Ionian Islands.

Despite this ignominious exit from the affairs of Greece and the distrust aroused by his apparently treacherous alliance with Odysseus, Trelawny had nonetheless succeeded for a short time in living the kind of adventurous life which previously he had only enjoyed in his imagination. There were now enough stories with some basis of truth, even if grossly exaggerated, to add to his fictionalised past as a buccaneer, for Trelawny as the friend of Shelley and Byron to dine out for the rest of his long life. When he died in 1881, the last relic of the romantic age, he was buried alongside Shelley in the Protestant cemetery at Rome in the position which with great forethought he had arranged for himself almost sixty years before.

There is one curious postscript to be added to the account of Trelawny's association with Tithorea. In the village there is a man whose surname is Andreou but who carries the nickname

Trelawnis. It is a nickname that has been handed down from father to son for generations and can only recall the Englishman. No one knows its origin for certain. It has been suggested that the Andreou of that time gave help in some way to the wounded Trelawny, perhaps providing herbs or food. There is the more obvious explanation of a line of descent from an illegitimate child. Whatever the explanation the name will soon disappear as its present tenant has no descendants.

*

It takes about two hours to walk from Tithorea to Amphiclia. From the central square in Tithorea you walk in the opposite direction from that to the cave of Androutsos and proceed along the other arm of the T, past the small hotel and out of the village. It's a pleasant walk along a track which passes first through olive trees and then endless bushes of holly oak, high above the Cephisian plain. Finally the way cuts straight across the ridge, around which the main road and the railway are forced to travel, and arrives at the top of the slope above Amphiclia or Dadi.

Approached by this way Amphiclia makes a far more favourable impression than that received by a visitor arriving by road at the modern end of the town. As I walked down the street to the central square of the upper town, the Plateia Parnassou, I noticed many of the older style of Roumeliot houses, stone-built with tiled roofs and many with large wooden balconies. The design of such houses is remarkably simple. The living quarters are placed on the first or second floor level as indicated by the balconies, while the lower parts are reserved for shops, storerooms or, more particularly in villages, for stables. The conventional two-storey arrangement (by no means limited to Roumelia), which neatly separated the humans on the first floor from their animals and stores on the floor below, goes back to the Turkish period and was itself a refinement of single-storey cottages of an even more functional character. These usually consisted of one large room; at one end of this there was generally a raised wooden platform where the family might live and sleep around an open hearth, and the rest of the space was occupied at night by the animals. You will not see today many examples of such single-room houses, at least in their original form, but we get an amusing description of a night spent in one, in fact the khan at Chaironia, in the pages of William Mure in the middle of the nineteenth century: 'The accommodation differed little from that of other places of the same class previously described; with the exception that the body of the low dark shed was filled with cattle instead of men...As there was no other human guest but our party I established exclusive possession of the small wooden platform here raised but two or three feet above the ground and of the mud hearth in its centre...My slumbers were a little disturbed by the midnight gambols of the more lively portion of my fellow-lodgers some of whom amused themselves chasing each other up and down the building.'†

Even in the newer two-storey buildings living remains primitive enough. Many are without running water or sanitation, the oven is situated picturesquely but inconveniently outside and they are frequently full of rats. At Amphiclia few of these traditional houses are particularly old, but in a country where with good reason owing to the poor methods of construction a house is described as palaio (old) if it predates the last war, their days are numbered. As they decay, they will be replaced by the more enduring terrazas.

From the upper plateia the continuation of the road from Tithorea, known initially as Odhos Mitropoleos, leads past the Metropolitan church of the Panagia which is of basilical form with a handsome campanile, and if followed will bring you out on the west of the town to the cemetery. This has been placed somewhat dramatically on part of the remains of the acropolis of the ancient city of Amphiclia. The acropolis lay on a low triangular plateau which rises only slightly above the surrounding land, rather like that of Elatia on the other side of the valley of the Cephisos. Almost all traces of the walls have gone on the western and northern sides, but on the east some stretches remain to three courses high (in trapezoidal style) and on the south, beside the road, part of the circuit constructed with very large blocks is preserved to a height of about 2 metres, forming at this point the wall of the modern cemetery. The base of a square tower here projects from the line of the wall and this is now crowned to great effect by a large piece of ornate wrought iron decorating the grave of some modern Amphiclian.

Inside the cemetery the most prominent object is a ruined mediaeval tower built at its lower level with a number of ancient blocks. In addition there is a small church, that of the Koimisis. It

†*Journal*, vol. 11. p. 217

was an inscription found within this building, which recorded the dedication of a statue in the precinct of the god Dionysos, that served to identify the ruins as being those of ancient Amphiclia. For Pausanias tells us that Dionoysis was honoured with 'orgies' at Amphiclia. Moreover the god also gave prophesies here through the medium of a priest. It is possible therefore that the church itself marks the site of the shrine of Dionysos.

*

The road past the cemetery leads up the hillside behind the town

The cemetery on the site of the former acropolis of Amphiclia

towards the Monastery of the Panagia and then continues to Phterolacca (from which the Ski Centre may be reached). Until recently the sides of Parnassos were here covered with extensive woods of fir and pine, but in the summer of 1977 they caught fire and were mostly destroyed. Amphiclia itself was threatened and the town nearly emulated the curious description in Pausanias of the appearance of the ancient city as resembling a burning pyre. The woods around the monastery were mostly burnt down, but its buildings were left undamaged. As I went up the blackened slopes to the monastery later that year, the gloomy scene was suddenly relieved at one point in the road by the sight of as many as a hundred villagers, many of them women in gaily coloured clothes, already working to restore their forest by digging holes for the new trees.

The Monastery of the Panagia, a nunnery for the last twenty years or more, is another triumph of enterprise and housewifely orderliness. In recent years the Mother Superior has supervised the rebuilding of almost the entire monastery apart from the church, and neat new cells with verandahs decorated with flowers now surround the central Katholicon. The first monastery on this site dated from the Byzantine period but was totally rebuilt in about 1756, and of that rebuilding only the Katholicon remains. The church is dedicated to the Birth of the Panagia and has its festival on 8 September. Inside the building the eighteenth century wall-paintings have almost all gone except in the narthex where on the east wall there is a large representation of the Last Judgment or Second Coming. Here an enthroned Christ sits in judgment over the dead, together with his apostles. To one side we see Paradise, and on the other the fiery waters of Hell which is shown brimful with sinners, devils and lechers. In the naos, where the Mother Superior has herself over many years built a fine gilded plaster-work screen, there is a wonder-working icon of the Panagia. Tradition says the icon was discovered outside the monastery under a piece of ground where water was exuding, and at Advent it is taken down to the town to be paraded around the houses, as also happens on other occasions when it is required to cure the sick.

*

The old road from Amphiclia to the next village of Polidrosos, otherwise known as Kato Suvala, diverges from the asphalt road to the monastery just past the cemetery and again cuts across a ridge that here reaches out towards the Cephisos. In earlier years the villagers of Polidrosos, being without shops of any kind, used frequently to travel to Dadi by this way, and it only takes about one and a half hours to walk to the village by an easy route. When finally you turn the flank of the hill you catch sight of a great cluster of cypress trees and almost as many terrazas with their flat roofs that reflect the afternoon sun. This is Polidrosos, and the village is tucked into one of the several valleys along the huge re-entrant which lies to the east of the spur of Gerolacca at the most northerly point of Parnassos. Down in the plain the ribbon of asphalt carries on to the village of Lilaia or Kato Agoriani and then continues around Gerolacca to Gravia and the pass to Amphissa. To the east of the salient the territory once belonged to the Phocians, and to the north where the valley is finally trapped between Oiti and Kallidromon lay the Tetrapolis of ancient Doris.

From Polidrosos (which has little to detain one) I was aiming for the ruins of ancient Lilaia to the south of the modern village. First however I followed an asphalt road that proceeds southwest from Polidrosos and terminates near one of the sources of the Cephisos. This only takes about half an hour to reach, and it is worth the detour. It was at this spring, which rises below a long artificial terrace at the base of the hills, that the ancient Greeks evidently placed the source of the Cephisos, although there are other sources higher up the river to the west. The source was in the territory of the ancient city of Lilaia, and thus we find a description of the river pouring 'its fair-flowing waters from Lilaia' in the Hymn to Apollo.

The terrace of polygonal walling, some 60 metres long, supported at its eastern end a building of ashlar masonry, of which two courses remain. This was probably a temple of the river god. The building was later converted into a Christian church, as evidenced by the outlines of the apses which have been added to the original plan. Below the terrace, the water from the spring now collects in a large basin before seeping away into a marshy area beyond it. From the former temple you look north across the valley, which is sprinkled with poplars and cypresses, to the mountains of Locris. It is a beautiful place and is entirely quiet except for the occasional sound of a bird in the rushes and the distant sheep bells on the hillside.

About 140 metres to the east of the source there are the remains of another building constructed with large regular blocks. This was plainly an Early Christian or Byzantine church of basilical form, and it probably took some of its material from the ancient structure above the spring. Various cross motifs may be seen at the doorway in the western end and on the lintel over the doorway into the main part of the church. Inside there is a profusion of columns and other architectural features including a square capital with a simple acanthus leaf design. It is now known locally as Ayia Eleousa.

Fourth century BC walling of the acropolis of Lilaia

From this point the ruins of the acropolis of ancient Lilaia are clearly visible to the west on the edge of a ravine. It takes a further half an hour to cross the bed of the torrent issuing from the ravine and then to walk across fields to the base of the rocky hillside holding the citadel. A long wall, substantially preserved in places, descends the hillside towards a bend in the road leading to the modern village, and this structure appears to have been designed to link the true acropolis at the highest point of the wall with the city itself (of which only few signs remain) in the plain below. The wall simply fenced in on the west a small strip of sloping land which was protected on the east by the precipices above the ravine; at the top it then made a right-angled return to the south towards the ravine's edge, thus creating a small fortified enclosure within the angle.

It is just possible to make your way through the undergrowth to the top. Along the line of the west wall there are the remains of four towers and much of the wall is preserved on both faces; at the steepest part it stands to the original height of nearly 6 metres, nine or ten courses high, with the coping stones still in position. The south face of the acropolis has two towers; the west tower is some 12 metres high but the upper part is mediaeval. The style of masonry is as ever trapezoidal. Somehow the city escaped the ravages of Xerxes along the Cephisos, but like the other Phocian cities it had be rebuilt after destruction by the Macedonians.

It is possible to start out from the level ground above this remarkable ruin to walk to Eptalophos (or Ano Agoriani) higher on the mountain. You first strike across the connecting ridge to the west and then turn up towards the rocky hill to the south, thereby gaining the old path between the two related villages of Ano (Upper) and Kato (Lower) Agoriani. The path, its edges lined with stones, winds in zig-zags to the top of the hills. Then after passing a pocket of cultivated land it joins the new road from the plain for the last leg into the village. The contrast was particularly sharp on this occasion between the old path and the new road, so different in scale, the one conforming to the contour of the land, the other proceeding almost in spite of it. I met one fellow traveller on the old road, a woman who was riding a mule and leading another animal which was carrying a plough. Evidently she was returning from her fields in the lower village after a day spent at work on her land. It is a journey of about one and a half hours.

Eptalophos stands in a wooded hollow among the heights of

Parnassos at the head of the ravine that disgorges below ancient Lilaia. The village is at about the same altitude as Arachova but is even cooler in summer since it faces north and lies among fir trees. Coachloads of visitors, lured by the shade and by the streams of spring water, come here then to escape from the suffocating streets of Athens, and the small plateia filled with plane trees has several restaurants.

*

There is a path from Eptalophos through the fir forests towards Kalania which would have been the most direct route to Delphi. Kalania is a summer retreat for some of the inhabitants of Delphi and is a collection of huts, with a spring and a chapel nearby, situated in a large clearing to the west of Paliovouna, approximately midway between Eptalophos and Delphi. The path to Kalania later joins a forest road that then emerges on the tableland above Delphi and it would take about half a day to walk to Delphi by that way. For once I took seriously the suggestion at Eptalophos that I should never find the path, and instead toiled up the main road from Agoriani to Arachova as it wound through the trees towards Livadi.

Among the low hills that form the prelude to Livadi a dirt road leads off the main road to the right to go towards Palaiovouna, the hill on which the Corycian Cave is situated. You must also strike the same track if you are coming from Arachova in the opposite direction. If you walk along this, shortly before the point where the country opens out and the road begins to work along the north side of the plain, a branch to the right travels up Palaiovouna to arrive just below the cave. Alternatively you may stay on the level ground around the base of the hill, until you draw near to a chapel by a grove of large holly oaks where a sign indicates a precipitous path up the hillside to the cave. To this point below the hill takes about three and a half hours from Eptalophos.

(It takes about three hours to reach the Corycian Cave from Delphi. You must find the bottom of the Kake Skala, the paved path previously mentioned, by climbing up to the fort of Philomelos to the west of the sanctuary and walking towards the hillside. It takes about an hour to reach the top of the Kake Skala. There you proceed northwards along a natural fold in the land to some watering troughs, where you turn east and find a dirt road skirting the wooded valley before you. The cave is on the more northerly of two hills that form a gap in the distance, and you continue on the road until you reach the chapel beyond which the path to the cave is signposted).

The Corycian Cave is situated about 150 metres above the plateau of Livadi. The view from the mouth of the cave looks over the Gulf of Corinth in one direction and in the other, beyond the fields of Livadi, it embraces the whole flank of Gerontovrachos — those heights of Parnassos where Pausanias says the Thyiad women raved above the clouds in honour of Dionysos and Apollo. The cave itself was sacred to Pan and the Nymphs, and an inscription on a stone on one side of the entrance records a dedication to these companions of Dionysos. From its narrow entrance the cave then opens out into an immense chamber, 60 or more metres long and up to 12 metres high, furnished with slowly dripping stalactites and stalagmites. For the fanciful these immense pillars might easily assume the shapes of Pan and the Nymphs, and among the many, mostly modest, offerings found in excavations inside the cave (and now exhibited in Room 13 of the Delphi Museum) one of the most charming is a group of terracotta figurines representing the Nymphs dancing around Pan's double-flute. Beyond this first great gothic hall there are reputedly many further rooms, which have given rise to the name of the cave as Sarantavli or Forty-Chambered, and it was to the Corycian Cave that the inhabitants of Delphi fled at the time of Xerxes, as did many during the War of Independence.

And the Thyiads, of whom we have heard nothing since Panopeos, did their mad chase across the heights above Delphi bring them up the rocky slope to the Corycian Cave? We do not know exactly, but from our vantage point above Livadi we may catch a glimpse of their wanderings on the mountain.

It will be remembered that the Thyiads from Athens travelled every two years in the autumn to attend the Dionysian celebrations, and here they joined their sister celebrants from Delphi. The festival was of considerable importance. Dionysos enjoyed a position at Delphi no less honoured than Apollo, and Plutarch, at one time the priest at Delphi, declared that the sanctuary belonged equally to both gods. The grave of Dionysos lay in the adyton of the temple of Apollo, and during Apollo's absence in the three winter months from November to February the oracle was silent and Dionysos was worshipped in his stead. After the sun

Shepherd on Parnassos

god had left for the north a mysterious ceremony took place under the guidance of the Thyia, the priestess of Dionysos, celebrating the rebirth of the god through whose obscure powers the dead winter vine might be coaxed back into life and the vegetation renewed. Then in the biennial Dionysian festival the god's worshippers, for at least one brief night, left behind their well-regulated existence and abandoned themselves to the irrational forces within their own personalities in an attempt to identify themselves with the vitality and even the person of the god himself.

Dionysos had no temple at Delphi, although two small buildings immediately to the east of the theatre may have been dedicated to the god as chapels or shrines. His only temple was the theatre itself, an institution which had originated from the dances and mummery of the early Dionysian festivals. The theatre at Delphi dates from the fourth century BC and from that time at least we can imagine the young Thyiads dancing there in honour of the god late on an afternoon in November, as the cliffs of the Phraedriades caught fire in the last of the sun. They moved to the compulsive rhythm of the dithyramb, and their cheeks were soon flushed with refreshing draughts of wine from the new harvest. Carried away by their enthusiasm the young women sang and hymned the presence of the god until they imagined themselves the legendary maenads of his company. Then with shouts of 'Bromios', the mystic name of Dionysos, and amid the continuing clamour of flute and drum a torchlit procession began to climb the paved path above the sanctuary towards the heights of Parnassos.

The maenads carried aloft the ivy-garlanded wand of Dionysos, the thyrsus, and accompanying them were other members of his retinue, a masked revel of horned Pans, of Satyrs rudely covered by goatskins and of drunken Sileni, all to be the indiscreet partners of the Thyiads' celebrations. Even Bacchos himself was present, in the form of a young man, to lead them in their rout. Once on Parnassos the Thyiads roamed under the light of their torches across the valleys in the direction of the Corycian Cave and the plain of Livadi, calling upon the god, perhaps at times stopping to dance, until at last they found their victim, some animal such as a young kid that they might tear to pieces and devour raw in an ecstasy of violence. In this final act they sought the ultimate communion with the god whom they believed to be immanent in every living creature. Then, exhausted, they would slowly retrace their steps to Delphi. Sometimes they became lost or were overtaken by a snowstorm and had to be rescued from the mountain.

Whether on this occasion the young god took physical possession of some of his followers or they gave themselves to the swift embrace of his male companions, there was certainly some degree of sexual freedom during the festival. In the *Ion* of Euripides, Xouthos having once stayed at Delphi for the Bacchic mysteries imagines Ion to be the child of his drunken partnership with a maenad. However the word orgy has become so overlaid in our minds with sexual connotations, that we can easily forget its original meaning of mysteries or secret rites in honour of a god, and we should remember that the sexual licence when it occurred was really secondary to the central purpose of becoming closer to the deity.

The Kake Skala descending to Delphi

*

It is an easy walk of about two hours or so from below the Corycian Cave to the sanctuary of Apollo, downhill all the way. You simply follow the road through the firs until finally you arrive at some watering troughs where you take the path down the centre of a fold in the land. This area is known generally as Kroki, and the small valley appears like a mild echo of the great cleft in the cliffs above Delphi. At its bottom you are close to the top of the Phraedriades and here you must go to the right to obtain the Kake Skala. Sometime before this point, in fact near the watering troughs, you lose sight of the summits of Parnassos, and I paused here to gain one last view of the long outline of the mountain which is hidden from sight at Delphi by the high cliffs of the Phraedriades. There is something completely sublime about Parnassos when viewed from this side. It is at once both peaceful and majestic. The towering edifices of the east have disappeared and instead the summits assume the profile of a reclining figure, a female form lying quietly at rest. It might be the ancient world asleep.

The Kake Skala, the paved road that descends in great sweeps down the hillside above the stadium, certainly goes back to antiquity. Its name (Bad Steps or Staircase) can only be explained by the effort involved in climbing it since it is beautifully constructed. Mostly it is paved but some of the steps have been hewn out of the rock. At various points shortcuts have been made between the longer sections. There is too an ancient watercourse which descends the hill almost vertically and can make descent even quicker, although this is a little dangerous.

The path arrives at the very top of the ridge which carries the fort of Philomelos, high above the stadium. We have at last come to Delphi.

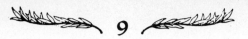

9
DELPHI

The site of Delphi lies high above the deep valley of the Pleistos, immediately below the two huge limestone cliffs known in antiquity as the Phraedriades, the Shining Rocks. At the junction of these twin heights, which here form a sharp angle in the southern wall of Parnassos, the winter torrents falling from above have created a great cleft where even in summer the water still percolates through the stone to feed the Castalian spring. On either side of the Castalian cleft, at the base of the cliffs, the terraced slopes filled with olive trees fall steeply away to the Pleistos gorge, beyond which rises the dark flank of Cirphis, flat and perspectiveless, like the mute scenery of a theatre. The often noted theatre-like effect of the Shining Rocks extends over the whole valley, so that the recess in the cliffs has for its backcloth the shadows of the gorge and the precipices of Cirphis. There is perhaps nowhere else where there exists such a satisfying relationship between all the elements in one's physical surroundings.

This extraordinary natural beauty of Delphi makes all the greater impact on the visitor owing to the manner in which the site is (usually) first glimpsed. Both from the west and from the east it comes suddenly into view, thereby enhancing its feeling of seclusion and mystery at the very centre of things. From the east the road from Arachova has to turn a corner of the mountain face before finally allowing a view across the edge of the valley to the area of the sanctuary. From the west the effect is even more dramatic, for it is only when the ridge on the west of Delphi has been mounted (as in the past) or rounded (as today) that the recess holding the sanctuary and the one time city of Delphi opens to the eye. Until that triumphant moment Delphi remains entirely hidden behind the hill of Philomelos (as we shall call the western ridge) and is invisible from the bay of Crisa from which so many visitors must have come in the past.

The same features that contribute so forcefully to the unique situation of Delphi have not always made a comfortable home for those who have settled on the site. In summer the Phraedriades and the hill of Philomelos create between them an airless cauldron, burned by the sun throughout the day (hence the ancient proverb concerning empty discussion, 'to dispute about a shadow in Delphi'), while in winter the long valley draws strong winds and storms. In this rugged landscape there is little cultivable land, and it is clear that the early settlements at Delphi can only ever have occurred in association with some important religious cult.

The choice of the dramatic site of Delphi as a centre of cult worship was perhaps obvious enough, particularly when we learn that the earliest object of worship was the Earth Goddess, but an important prerequisite was precisely its position astride the principal east-west route through central Greece. The early travellers journeyed this way between the Gulf of Corinth and the centres in Boeotia, and as today probably refreshed themselves from the sharp water of the Castalian, although some must have followed the bottom of the valley to the watershed of the Pleistos to the east of modern Arachova. It is not difficult to imagine the awesome effect of such a place on their impressionable minds, and when a cult was eventually established here it was bound to receive the attention of many of the travellers. The establishment and success of a religious cult at Delphi thus rested to a considerable extent on the paradoxical fact that while lying on an important trade route it possessed an atmosphere of great seclusion and mystery owing to its extraordinary physical surroundings. To the Greek mind such an atmosphere was only explicable in terms of the supernatural. Plato, one of the admirers of the oracle, described this feeling in simple terms when he said 'in fact the place seemed to be sacred'.

*

The Pleistos river flows out of the gorge below Delphi and continues through the olive groves on the plain in the direction of the sea at Kirrha. The Pleistos — 'the full stream' — now only carries any water after rain and what little it holds is lost among the fields before it reaches the sea. Yet at one time it was a more permanent feature, and not far from the eventual mouth of the stream, on a low eminence called the Magoula, French archaeologists in the 1930s found evidence of a large settlement dating from the Early Helladic period (or earlier) down to the early part of the Late Helladic or Mycenaean period. This town, which we may call

Kirrha from its classical successor, had links with the interior, particularly during the Middle Helladic period when for instance we find a large amount of Minyan pottery from Orchomenos. During the same period an acropolis was built on the spur near the modern town of Chriso, commanding the whole coastal plain as well as the routes through the Pleistos valley. The two cities — the one by the sea and the other inland — probably enjoyed the same territory and were in effect complementary to each other, although at different times one of the cities might predominate. Throughout Middle Helladic times the larger city remained by the sea, but in the Mycenaean period the centre of gravity moved to the large Cyclopean enceinte of Crisa much of which still remains to be seen near the church of Ayios Georgios. Finally in common with the other Mycenaean centres Crisa was destroyed by invaders from the north, by which time Kirrha had already sunk into obscurity.

The two related cities of Crisa and Kirrha were thus at the western end of the trade route on which Delphi lay, and their existence like that of the important Boeotian centres at the further end of the route long predated any development at the site of the oracle. At Delphi both the first settlement, which was on the site of the eventual Sanctuary of Apollo, and the earliest discovered area of cult worship in the region of the later Temple of Athena Pronaia belong solely to the Mycenaean period. By that time the ancient city of Krisa was already an important Mycenaean centre. The poet of the Homeric *Hymn to Apollo*, writing long after the destruction of Crisa by the Dorians, was accurately reflecting the reality of earlier times when he described the god arriving in the territory of Crisa to build his temple: 'Further yet you went, far-shooting Apollo, until you came to the town of the presumptuous Phlegyae who dwell on this earth in a lovely glade near the Cephissian lake, caring not for Zeus. And thence you went speeding swiftly to the mountain ridge, and came to Crisa beneath snowy Parnassus, a foothill turned to the west; a cliff hangs over it from above and a hollow, rugged glade runs under. There the lord Apollo resolved to make his lovely temple.'† For at that distant time Delphi had stood under the shadow of its far larger neighbour — and it was a problem she was to face again in the historical period.

*

†1.277f. Translated by Evelyn-White (Loeb edition)

The *Hymn to Apollo* naturally gave precedence to the male deity who it describes coming to Delphi from Olympos and establishing his temple there after slaying a she-serpent. However a later literary tradition spoke of other deities before Apollo, notably Ge or Earth, and it is clear that the earliest cult centred upon worship of the Earth Goddess. Many terracotta figurines of the female form have been found from the late Mycenaean period (to be seen in one of the showcases in Room 1 of the Museum),† and a connection with Crete and its cult of the Mother Goddess is suggested by the discovery of a Minoan lioness-head rhyton in a deeper layer under the Sanctuary of Apollo. (There is a Cretan element too in the *Hymn to Apollo*, when the poet describes the god in the form of a dolphin bringing Cretan sailors to become priests of his new temple.) Poseidon, the 'Earth-shaker', was also worshipped together with the Earth Goddess, and the conjunction of the two deities in a place of such natural beauty, in the middle of the seismic area of Greece, needs no further explanation.

The arrival of Apollo as a new-comer at Delphi was by no means welcomed, and the struggle for control of the shrine was told in the story of the slaying of the female serpent, itself a manifestation of the Earth. It is unclear where Apollo originated, although it was certainly outside Greece; in the *Iliad* he is shown as an enemy of the Greeks, while some traditions associated him with Lycia in Asia Minor and others with the north. Whatever his precise origin the god probably arrived with the Dorians from the north, and the seizure of the shrine at Delphi by his followers was but one aspect of the disturbances caused by the invaders throughout most of continental Greece.

The serpent nonetheless left a legacy behind. The name Pytho was bestowed on the site from its rotting corpse (from the Greek 'pytho', rot) and from this the serpent later became known in turn as Python. The omphalos, originally a fetish stone and eventually the subject of the classical myth of the meeting point of the two eagles of Zeus at the centre of the earth, was also sometimes thought of as being the tomb of the Python, just as the tripod on which the Pythia sat was said variously to contain the bones of Python or Dionysos. Thus the new deity was not allowed to forget his violence against the Earth's serpent, and by the classical period at

†A plan of the Delphi Museum is to be found at Appendix III, together with a list of its principal contents.

least his manner of appropriating the shrine was seen to have been wrong — hence the tradition of Apollo having to seek purification in the vale of Tempe, as commemorated in the festival of the Stepterion.

There were other respects too in which the pre-Apolline divinities were remembered or propitiated. In the archaic period the Earth Goddess retained a sanctuary close to the temple of Apollo near the rock of the Sybil. The Temple of Athena Pronaia, built in the area of the previous cult of the Earth, also continued the tradition of worship of a female goddess. Another feature was the use here by Apollo of a female servant as the mouthpiece of his oracles, whereas in his other oracular centres he was served by male priests, and this might perhaps represent the continuation of a line of priestesses who had earlier served the Earth Goddess. Nor was Poseidon forgotten. The god who had shared Delphi with the Earth Goddess kept an altar within the Temple of Apollo.

In short, Apollo a male deity imported into Greece most probably by northern invaders displaced the Earth Goddess at the end of the Mycenaean period, but despite the savage destruction of Mycenaean cities such as Crisa and the cultural disintegration throughout Greece at that time the intruder was not strong enough to capture entirely the hearts and minds of the worshippers of the old shrine. To win acceptance Apollo was forced to compromise with the older deities.

*

The oracle of Apollo appears to have been established on its historical site during the eighth century BC and the first stone temple, built according to tradition by Trophonius and Agamedes, was constructed in the seventh century. The growing reputation of the oracle started to bring enquirers from many parts of Greece and abroad, cities and individuals alike. Many of the colonies sent overseas by the Greeks during this early period came to be associated with Delphic oracles, and even if the foundation oracles were mainly invented some time after the event they still show the importance that soon attached to Delphi. During the seventh century the oracle's fame was sufficiently widespread that not only a Greek ruler like Cypselus, the tyrant of Corinth, but several oriental monarchs such as Midas of Phrygia and Gyges of Lydia (so it was said) sent large gifts to Apollo.

During this early period, the oracle though already wealthy remained prey to the archaic city of Kirrha (by the sea) which controlled the approach from the west. For many states, especially those in the Peloponnese, the approach to Delphi by sea to the Gulf of Crisa was more convenient than the land route from the east, and the successor to the domains of Mycenaean Crisa was able to levy tolls on those visitors to Apollo arriving in this way. The war which eventually resulted from this conflict of interests was known as the Crisaean War, and it has often been supposed that the war was directed against a city on the site of Mycenaean Crisa. However the excavations by the French at Crisa have demonstrated that Crisa was never reoccupied after its destruction by the Dorians and that it must have been the archaic city of Kirrha whose power was broken at the end of the so-called Crisaean war. Surprisingly there has never been found any trace of archaic Kirrha, and the excavations at the modern village have shown that the remains of the classical port of Delphi lay directly on top of the Bronze Age settlement.

The prosecutors of the war against Kirrha were the members of the Amphictyonic League, an old assembly of many of the peoples of Greece including the inhabitants of Phocis and Boeotia. The cities of these different areas took it in turns to send representatives to the meetings of the League at Pylai (Thermopylai) and, later, at Delphi. The city of Delphi, which lay on the terraces below the Sanctuary of Apollo, was far too small to deal with the port of Kirrha and the Amphictyonic states decided to take the responsibility for the war upon themselves. The port was finally captured after a long siege in about 590 BC and its territory which chiefly comprised the large inland plain was consecrated to Apollo. Except for occasional short-lived incursions the land remained uncultivated throughout antiquity and in his day Pausanias described the plain as being bare. Its only use was to provide pasture for the horses and oxen belonging to the city and temple of Delphi; most of the cattle, once fattened on the rich grass, would have been destined for sacrifice to Apollo. Not a single olive tree would have then graced the view from Delphi across the plain to the sea. And henceforward Kirrha itself would only exist, on a different site, as the port of Delphi.

Other changes, as significant, followed upon the conclusion of the war. The Delphians, under the protection of the League, acquired a totally independent position, freed even from their old tribal unit the Phocians. The inter-tribal nature of the Amphictyony helped the oracle to acquire its pan-Hellenic status. The Pythian festival was reorganised to take place every four years, with the addition of many musical and athletic contests, and it would now draw competitors from all over the Greek world. The Sanctuary of Apollo was soon to become the treasure house and art gallery of Greece. According to tradition the most magnificent of the gifts at this time came from Croesus, the king of Lydia. He sent gifts to other oracles but reserved the best for Delphi after he had tested its veracity. The king sent over a hundred ingots of gold, a golden statue of a lion of immense weight, two great mixing-bowls — one of gold, another of silver — which were placed on either side of the entrance of the temple, a female figure in gold and among other treasures jewellery belonging to his queen. In the story told by Herodotos the motive for these gifts was clearly to obtain a favourable answer to his question of the oracle about the projected expedition against Persia. The famous response, that if the king marched against the Persians he would destroy a great empire, which Croesus took to be that of his enemies but turned out to be his own, is one of many spectacular predictions attributed to Delphi. Unfortunately like most of the others it is probably fictional.

The first of the treasuries built to house under one roof the offerings of a particular community was that of Cypselus the tyrant of Corinth, which was dedicated in the seventh century. In the sixth century others were added, including those of Sicyon, Cnidos and Siphnos. In 548 BC the stone temple reputedly built by Trophonius was destroyed by fire, and a new temple was completed towards the end of the sixth century with contributions from throughout Greece and from abroad (including Amasis, the king of Egypt). Through the munificence of the contractors for the temple, the Alcmaeonid family of Athens, the building was given a marble facade. After the Greek victories over the Persians the god received many new dedications including the treasury of the Athenians and the monument of the battle of Plataia.

By this time the sanctuary had assumed a form which we might recognise today and had begun to fill with the statues of the god Apollo and of the famous men of Greece that were the admiration of every visitor. Delphi had become one of the most important centres in the entire Greek world. The principal cost of such an exalted position was that the oracle too readily became the target of the ambitions of the city-states, and in particular of Athens in the fifth century and of the Phocians in the fourth.

*

When visitors to Delphi had arrived at the new port of Kirrha they proceeded across the empty plain and then up the escarpment carrying the ruins of Mycenaean Crisa. After a long climb they at last arrived abreast the ridge which lies to the west of Delphi and saw for the first time below the twin Phraedriades the entire Sanctuary of Apollo. Something of the same effect may still be gained by following the line of the old road from Chriso as it approached the former village of Delphi. Until the end of the nineteenth century when the village of Delphi was moved to its present position, its houses were situated on the site of the Sanctuary of Apollo, and the road to Delphi from Chriso entered the village past the small church of Ayios Elias. It is almost certain that this approach also coincided with the ancient route.

Today from the central church of Ayios Nicolaos situated in the middle of Delphi you follow the signposts towards the Stadium. The street up which you walk is named after Angelos and Eva Sikelianos. On the left as you proceed there are the rock tombs noticed by Byron and other European travellers. Near the top of the incline there stands a large isolated villa which once belonged to the poet Sikelianos, and from close to this the cleft in the Phraedriades, which until that moment has been hidden by the hill of Philomelos, can at last be seen rising above the cypresses surrounding Ayios Elias. The same trees now largely obscure the area of the sanctuary below, but formerly at this point the visitor's eye was almost level with the roof of the Temple of Apollo and could range over the terracotta tiles of the treasuries and porticoes which mounted the terraces up to the theatre and the Cnidian Clubhouse at the top of the precinct. On the buildings the architectural embellishments and sculptured decorations were picked out in bright colours of blue, blood-red and ochre against the resplendent white of the marble, and between them there could be glimpsed many of the countless offerings to Apollo, mostly statues, some of gold or delicately patinated bronze, others of brightly painted marble or terracotta, standing like a mute pageant of the ancient world. Yet at this distance, for all the wealth of display, the objects within the sanctuary could not entirely occupy one's gaze.

The most striking feature was their incomparable natural setting with which in some mysterious way they succeeded in remaining in harmony, observing that sense of proportion between the works of man and of god or nature so important to the Greeks and now so lacking in the modern world.

*

In antiquity the meeting point between mortals and the spiritual force or god that was felt to be particularly at home at Delphi was the famous oracle. We might then attempt to follow the steps of an enquirer from his arrival to the moment of consultation.

Our enquirer is an Athenian of, say, the third century BC. He is a wealthy trader, who wishes to consult the god on some private matter such as a proposed sea journey abroad or his continuing lack of a male child. At Athens, as a man of some importance, he has managed to arrange with one of the agents of the oracle in the city that he will be able to consult the Pythia on the appointed day of the month for a verbal reply rather than use the everyday system of the lot-oracle. And so towards the end of the previous month the Athenian set out on horse with a retinue of servants, travelling by Thebes, Lebadea and the Schist Road, so as to reach the oracle some days before the seventh of the month, the date when the Pythia gave her replies from her seat in the Temple of Apollo.

Approaching Delphi from the east they came first to one of the city's cemeteries, much in the same way as they had left Athens past the Kerameikos. Across the valley beyond the Castalian cleft they could see the township itself descending in terraces below the road, while occupying the highest part of the city there was the Sanctuary and the Temple of Apollo, with some of the few remaining gold ornaments still catching the afternoon sun. But no visitor arriving here, and particularly an Athenian, could disregard the group of buildings which lay immediately to the left of the road and which comprised the Sanctuary of Athena Pronaia. The epithet, meaning foretemple, referred to the relationship of this temple of the goddess to the great house of Apollo, and we may be sure that our Athenian would here step aside from the road to make a small gift to his native goddess in the hope of a successful outcome to his journey.

The gateway to the east of the precinct led to an area with several altars in front of the old Temple of Athena. In the third century this building was already in ruins. It had been built of tufa, in the Doric order, at the very beginning of the fifth century to replace a much earlier temple (of which some 'biscuit' capitals still survive) on the site of the original worship of the Earth Goddess. The temple had been first damaged by the fall of rocks in 480 which had discouraged the band of Persian marauders from advancing to plunder the Sanctuary of Apollo, and it had been finally ruined by the earthquake of 373. At the time of our visitor a good number of its columns were still standing, and so they remained for the excavators until 1905, when all but three were bowled over by more rocks which are still to be seen among the ruins. A newer temple to the goddess had been built in the fourth century at the other end of the precinct. This time it was of local stone and of a simpler design, with only six columns adorning the outside and without any sculptural decoration.

However before reaching the new Temple of Athena the visitor had to pass in front of three other buildings. First there were two small treasuries in Parian marble, the second of which, in the Ionic order and dedicated by the inhabitants of Massilia in about 530 BC, possessed an attention to detail characteristic of this period; we may still see the attractive moulding running around the outside of the building, while its two columns in antis had capitals of the Aeolic type ringed with palm leaves. Then there was the circular-shaped Tholos built in the fourth century from limestone and Pentelic marble. We do not know the precise purpose of the Tholos, nor do we know by whom it was dedicated, although we may have the name of the architect in one Theodoros of Phocaea (in Ionia) who was said to have written a treatise on this remarkable building. In the second century AD the building held the statues of several Roman emperors. The Tholos possessed twenty columns around the outside; above the architrave there were triglyphs and sculptured metopes and an elaborate cornice decorated with lions' heads. The external wall of the nave was also decorated with metopes and triglyphs, and at its base there was a delicate moulding of leaves. On the inside of the cella there were ten engaged Corinthian columns. Three of the external columns have now been restored, together with some replicas of the metopes and cornice, the fragmentary remains of which may be seen in Room 10 of the Museum. The entire building must have struck the ancient eye as forcibly as it strikes ours today both for its perfection of form and the welcome departure from the rectangular to the round.

At the new Temple of Athena the Athenian paused to make a libation of wine and to pray to the sculptured images of the goddess, entreating her to conduct him safely to the good counsels of Apollo. The Greek showed no obvious abasement but standing upright, with his head uncovered and palms uplifted, invoked the titles of the goddess, reminded her of his past devotions and then ended by entreating her favour. It was direct, even commercial — something he understood. In return for his gift of wine he expected her help.

Beyond the temple the path continued out of the precinct in the direction of the Gymnasium. The Athenian once practised here as a young man when competing in the Pythian Games, and so would have been amused to look again on the scenes of his youth. The area consisted of an upper and a lower terrace. On the upper level there were two practice running tracks; one which lay behind a stone colonnade was roofed, the other was entirely open, and both were the length of the Delphic stade (about 185 metres). The lower terrace had a large Palaestra for boxing and wrestling, comprised of a square court surrounded by an Ionic peristyle. On two of its sides there were several rooms, including one for changing. Next to the Palaestra there were the Baths. These had a round pool in the centre and basins against the retaining wall which were fed with cold water from decorative spouts. During the intervals between the Pythian Games, which were only held every four years, the young men of Delphi and any visitors to the city could continue to make use of the Gymnasium (as the whole area was known), and by the third century it was not unusual for visiting philosophers and orators to give lectures in the shade of the courtyard of the Palaestra.

It was over the Palaestra that the Monastery of the Panagia was ultimately built, partly from ancient materials. The monastery was a dependency of the Monastery of Jerusalem at Davlia and was visited by most of the European travellers, some of whom lodged here. In 1809 Byron and Hobhouse left their names on an ancient column lying in the northeast corner of the ruins. The monastery was removed at the beginning of the last century to make way for excavations, which revealed in addition to the structures known to our Athenian some hot baths built by the Romans.

The road above continued under the cliffs towards the Castalian spring. To the right was Hyampia, the height from which the Delphians to their shame had thrown poor Aesop on a trumped-up charge of embezzlement, probably for no greater sin than making fun of the priests. The spring itself lies well into the cleft between the two Phraedriades, and there is little doubt it was a place of worship from early times, since a statue base of the Earth Goddess has been found here and there were also stories connecting it both with the Python and with Apollo's return from Tempe. The fountain supplied by the spring was not always in the same place. In the archaic and classical periods the water from the spring was ducted into a sunken rectangular basin close to the side of the modern road; the water entered through the mouths of four brazen lions' heads mounted on one wall, and there were low benches on the other three sides. However by the third century it appears that the area immediately at the base of Hyampia (with which visitors to Delphi are most familiar) had been hewn out of the rock, creating a reservoir just in front of the source. Eight steps led down to the reservoir and this was fed by seven bronze lions' heads in the large slabs at the rear. Behind there were several niches in the rock which probably contained statuettes of various deities. In both cases the surplus spring water from the fountains joined any stream which flowed from the cleft and continued across the line of the road into the gorge below.

The function of the Castalian fountain has often been exaggerated. Its prime purpose at all times was that of ritual purification. We learn for example from Euripides in the *Ion* that its water was used to wash the Temple of Apollo and that the temple attendants also purified themselves by sprinkling water on their hair. We may presume that visitors did the same, although the structure of the two basins suggests that they bathed more of their body than just their heads. No doubt there was also some provision of water for drinking, but it was only a late and unreliable tradition in antiquity that connected the waters of the Castalian with poetic and then prophetic inspiration.

The Athenian just arrived in Delphi would have been sure to stop here both for refreshment and to cleanse himself, although the ritual purification before his formal approach to the oracle some days later would have necessarily required another visit. From the Castalian it was only a short distance to the city of Delphi itself, which spread on the terraces below the sanctuary unprotected by any city walls. As ever the narrow streets were full of visitors of many races, and the shopkeepers were out hawking their goods. Our visitor had no time to waste that afternoon as he had lodgings to find and he must seek out the Athenian proxenos or representative to ensure that the necessary arrangements for his consultation of the oracle would be put in hand. In the city much of the talk was of the boorishness of the Aetolians who were now, after the Macedonians, the masters of the Amphictyony.

When on one of the following days the Athenian visited the sanctuary he started from the principal entrance into the walled precinct, on the southeast corner (as today). He was probably accompanied by a guide who would have enlivened his description of the monuments with stories of past oracles. The gateway into the east wall which had been rebuilt in the fourth century was approached by some steps, on which were placed two large basins of holy water for the purification of the visitor, and it led directly onto the Sacred Way (as the path leading through the sanctuary has come to be known in modern times). The path then lay at a slightly higher level and consisted of steps between level stretches of pavement, the existing ramp being laid in the Roman or Byzantine period. Other passages led through the sanctuary but this was the route used by most visitors and processions.

In the third century BC Delphi was still at the height of its glory despite the removal of most of the gold by the Phocians. As late as the second century AD Pausanias found the sanctuary to be largely intact, although by then the treasuries were all empty and the oracle had suffered the depredations of the Romans. (Of these the Emperor Nero had been the worst; he was said to have carried away five hundred of the finest statues). It was Pausanias' description that allowed the identification of many of the monuments excavated by the French at the end of the nineteenth century.†

Many of the offerings first seen along the Sacred Way illustrated the rivalries among the Greek states, and they had been placed with more regard to their position in relation to the monuments of other cities than with any aesthetic concern. For example shortly on the left of the path was the offering of the Athenians erected after their victory over the Persians at Marathon, with sixteen statues. Later the Spartans managed to secure the prominent place between this monument and the gateway to commemorate their naval victory over the Athenians at Aegospotami in 404 BC. They set up no less than thirty-seven statues in bronze including those of

†A plan of the sanctuary is to be found at Appendix IV.

Zeus, Apollo and Poseidon (who was shown crowning the Spartan admiral Lysander) as well as of many of the Spartan captains and allies. But then immediately opposite that offering the Arcadians placed nine statues from the proceeds of their successful campaign against the Spartans in 369 when they were aided by the Thebans. Individual masterpieces as no doubt many of these statues were, they were crowded together in brightly coloured and (to our eyes at least) discordant disarray.

Towards the top of this leg of the Sacred Way was the first of the 'treasuries' dedicated to Apollo by the individual city-states. The buildings were mostly of similar design, like small temples, with two columns standing between the projecting ends of the two external walls (known as distyle in antis). Their function was varied: they served as a treasure house for many of the smaller, more portable offerings made by the city itself and also by its citizens; they formed an area where matters of public concern might be inscribed, such as boundary settlements, honorific decrees and the liberation of slaves; and they were convenient meeting places for visitors from among their own citizens who might here step aside amid the familiar collection of statues, tripods and spoils of war.

Three of these buildings may serve as examples for the remainder. The Treasury of Sicyon is the first, built about 500 BC of porous limestone in the Doric order. It was not a particularly impressive building, but excavation has found within its foundations parts of earlier buildings — some curved stonework (still visible in the ruins) from a round tholos-type structure, and some metopes of a rectangular building of about 560 BC (now displayed in Room 3 of the Museum). The five surviving metopes, all of mythological subjects, exemplify some of the main elements in archaic Greek art. In the two best preserved reliefs, that of Castor, Pollux and Idas (identified by coloured inscriptions) plundering cattle and that of the Calydonian Boar, we see the stylised treatment of the subjects, with details such as the hair, the eyes and muscles picked out with heavy incisions. The line of the figures is more important than the modelling as if a painting has been only lightly articulated in the round. Traces of colour are still visible on some of the slabs. Originally the black and dark-red of the figures stood out against the neutral background of the stone, with something of the effect of a black-figured vase painting of the same period.

Next to the Sicyonian treasury stood that of Siphnos, one of the richest in the precinct. From the large amount of its surviving decoration (in Room 5 of the Museum) we may still appreciate some of the impact made upon a visitor in antiquity. Built in about 525 BC of Parian marble out of a tithe of the revenues from the gold mines of the island of Siphnos, it was designed to demonstrate the wealth of its donors. From the carved egg and dart moulding at the base of the marble walls (still visible among the ruins) to the winged Victory astride the point of the roof, this treasury which was built in the Ionic order, with two lovely Caryatids replacing the conventional columns in the porch, succeeded in combining an elegance of design and sumptuousness of detail that were perfectly complementary. The Caryatids themselves, standing on plinths, with one hand drew back against their bodies the light chitons worn under the heavy folds of their cloaks, and with the other held out a piece of fruit or a flower. On their faces there was a serene smile and in their flowing hair small metal ornaments were planted, while on their heads they carried effortlessly a circular polos or hat decorated with nymphs and other figures, which supported in turn a cup-shaped capital with a representation of two lions tearing a stag. These two figures, brightly painted and glittering with their ornaments, stood against the shadows of the porch where an ornate doorway surrounded with a floral motif of lotus and palmette offered access inside the treasury. A similar design decorated the eaves above the pediment, and at the corners of the roof sat sphinxes above a line of lions' heads waterspouts. The pediment was filled with sculpture, and below this on the entablature above the Caryatids there ran a frieze between two further mouldings of astragali.

The frieze on the Siphnian treasury went around the whole building, but it was on the east side facing the visitor as he mounted the Sacred Way, and on the north overlooking him as he passed, that the sculpture was most striking. On the east there is a scene from the fighting in the Trojan War, viewed by the gods sitting in their partisan groups. On the north there is shown the war of the gods and giants. The figures (formerly identified by inscriptions), with their clothing and armour picked out in blue, green and red against a dark-blue background, surge across the battlefields in brilliant intersecting movements, attacking and in flight, stooping and falling. At one point a lion devours one of the giants, at another a Trojan groom holds in check four magnificent horses. Here the

The Treasury of the Athenians

artist has finally liberated the sculptures from the stone, and even if some of the archaic conventions persist (as in the facial expressions, the stylisation of hair and drapery, and the parallelism between the upper and lower parts of the body) these reliefs clearly differ from the static friezes on the south and west where a lesser artist is generally thought to have been at work.

One last building of this kind deserves mention and it was one that would have especially interested our visitor, namely the

Treasury of the Athenians. This stood higher up the Sacred Way, after the path had turned the corner past the Treasury of the Boeotians. The small Doric building, also of Parian marble, was constructed shortly after the battle of Marathon from a part of the spoils taken from the Persians, as we are told by the inscription on the platform to its south. Despite being overthrown by an earthquake and crushed by debris from the temple above, the building has been almost totally restored from the material once scattered around its ruins. The large number of inscriptions written across the blocks and also the differing thicknesses of the walls have allowed its reconstruction rather in the manner of a three-dimensional jigsaw puzzle. The building now offers much the appearance it would have done in the third century, except that it then possessed on the platform before it a pile of weapons and other Persian spoils and on the terrace to the east many small statues and inscription stelai. By that time the practice had also begun of inscribing honorific decrees on its walls. The two *Hymns to Apollo* now in Room 7 of the Museum were inscribed on the south wall of the treasury a century later.

It would have been scarcely necessary for any guide to point out to the Athenian the significance of the six metopes between the coloured triglyphs on the front face of the treasury. To an intelligent Greek the symbolism was obvious. Here there was shown the battle of the Athenians and Amazons, a legendary encounter clearly representing the victory of the Greeks over the barbarous Medes. On the important south side of the treasury the nine sculptured reliefs displayed the feats of Theseus, including the contest with Antiope, the death of the bull of Marathon and the killing of the Minotaur, while Heracles who was supplanted by Theseus as the national hero of Athens at the end of the sixth century had been relegated to the less obvious sides of the treasury on the west and the north. Today we see in place of these reliefs some plaster copies of the very fragmentary originals to be found in Room 6 of the Museum. Different hands have been detected in the remaining pieces, one style being identified as more conservative than the other, just as in the case of the Siphnian sculptures, but generally the metopes from the Athenian treasury represent the transition between the archaic and classical periods. It was a moment when the human form, now correctly observed and at times portrayed with great boldness of composition (as when Heracles is shown seizing the Hind of Ceryneia), is still graced with the last archaic smile.

Beyond the Athenian treasury the Sacred Way was increasingly dominated by the Temple of Apollo standing on a large terrace buttressed by a massive polygonal wall. This great wall was built in the sixth century at the time of the construction of the new Alcmaeonid temple, and was later covered with inscriptions recording the liberation of slaves. (A slave was liberated by the simple device of dedicating him or her to a god, in this case Apollo). Like the south wall of the sanctuary later known as the Hellenico, this wall was visible even before the excavations.

In front of the polygonal wall and behind the Council House of the city of Delphi there was a rocky area traditionally associated with the Earth Goddess where she retained some kind of sanctuary until at least the time of Plutarch. It was here that Apollo was said to have killed the Earth's servant, the Python, as it guarded her oracle. The Earth Goddess was believed to have given oracles at Delphi before the arrival of Apollo, and the large rock rent by a deep fissure from which it was thought that the Sibyl, an early itinerant prophetess, had once chanted, served to continue the tradition connecting this area with oracular activity. Even after the building of the polygonal wall in the sixth century had interfered with the north part of the Sanctuary of the Earth, the Delphic authorities were careful to preserve an ancient fountain immediately to the south of the temple which had long belonged to her precinct and from which for several centuries before the construction of the Cassotis fountain (in the fourth century) the Pythia possibly continued to drink before giving her prophesies. Then on another rock nearby there stood a tall column 10 metres high, carrying a superb Sphinx dedicated by the Naxians in about 570 BC (Room 5 of the Museum), a creature also associated with prophetic abilities. Thus this small part of the sanctuary had associations with the oldest history of Delphi and in particular with the powers of prophecy.

According to Plutarch the death of the Python was the subject of a mysterious drama called the Stepterion (or Septerion) enacted over eight years. This probably took place in a circular area surrounded by stone seats a little further up the Sacred Way, in front of the Stoa of the Athenians. The play was obscure even to Plutarch, but apart from the serpent's death the action appeared to represent Apollo's subsequent flight from Delphi, his purification in Tempe and his triumphant return crowned with laurel.

Of more immediate interest to our Athenian would have been the roofed colonnade built against the polygonal wall in front of him. This stoa, which was in the Ionic order with columns and capitals of Pentelic and Parian marble supporting a wooden architrave and roof, was dedicated by Athens at the close of the Persian Wars. The inscription in archaic lettering on the stylobate reads:

'The Athenians offered the stoa and the arms and the figureheads which they took from the enemy.'

The building is thought to have held the cables used by Xerxes to secure the bridging of the Hellespont as well as the trophies captured at the sea battle of Salamis. The portico later held spoils won by the Athenians from their fellow Greeks, and by the time of Pausanias the original purpose of the Stoa seems to have been forgotten as he attributes the relics to the Peloponnesian War.

Another war monument, that of the battle of Plataia, was placed in front of the temple to the east of the Sacred Way. In the third century only part of the dedication remained, though this was remarkable enough in itself, in the form of three intertwined serpents of bronze cast in a single piece and creating a vertical pillar. It had once supported a gold tripod — that is, a basin on three legs — but this had been melted down by the Phocians. The offering was furnished from the spoils of the battle of Plataia and had at first carried, probably on a stone pedestal, a vainglorious inscription recording the achievement of the Spartan commander Pausanias. Later, owing to the general indignation among the Greeks, this inscription was erased and replaced both by a list of the thirty-one cities who took any part in the war against the Persians (this being engraved on the coils of the serpent) and by a more general dedicatory inscription referring to the 'saviours of spacious Greece'.

The Plataian monument is an example of the damage done to the sanctuary by the Christian emperors. In the fourth century AD Constantine the Great carried off the serpent column to his new capital in the East, where it was set up and then used as a fountain in the Hippodrome. There it has remained ever since, with the bronze scarred by the marks of sabres and after the early eighteenth century without the serpents' heads. Yet in its truncated form it still stands over 5 metres tall. All that now remains at Delphi is part of the circular base of stone. (It is possible too that the gilt horses outside St Mark's Cathedral in Venice, which we know were carried away from Constantinople by the Fourth Crusade, came in the first place from a chariot dedicated at Delphi by the island of Rhodes and were also taken by Constantine).

From the spoils of Artemision and Salamis, we are told, the Greeks had also set up a great bronze Apollo holding in his hand the figurehead of a ship, and there were other war monuments on the terrace to the east of the temple, a site which attracted some of the richest offerings. At the point where the Sacred Way turns onto the terrace, there had once been placed tripods and Victories of gold offered by Gelon the tyrant of Syracuse and his three brothers as a memorial for their victory over the Carthaginians at the battle of Himera (480 BC), but these had been taken by the Phocians. Nearby, beyond one of the possible positions for the large acanthus column (Room 11 of the Museum) dedicated by the Athenians in the fourth century and beyond another huge statue of Apollo some 15 metres high, the Athenians had dedicated a bronze palm tree surmounted by a gilt Athena after their further successes against the Persians at the Eurymedon river in Asia Minor. Then there was the large altar (now restored) of mixed white and black marble given by the Chians in the early fifth century, which was probably the result of the islanders' gratitude after they had been freed from the Persians in 479.

Directly in front of the temple there was a forest of statues. Most were Apollos, but there were also statues of generals and war leaders as well as many images of animals, which by Pausanias' time included oxen, goats, lions and horses. Here too was the gilded statue of the courtesan Phryne made by her lover the fourth century sculptor Praxiteles. It stood near the altar, not far from the iron roasting-spits given by Rhodopis who had followed the same profession two centuries before. When many centuries afterwards Plutarch was showing a foreign visitor around the sanctuary, these two dedications by well-known prostitutes made the foreigner indignant. This caused one of the company to say of the statue of Phryne that Praxiteles ought rather to have been commended, 'because besides these golden kings he placed a golden courtesan, thus rebuking wealth for possessing nothing to be admired or revered'. Great beauty, for whatever purposes employed, was a prize only seldom given to mortals.

The fabulous gifts of the kings of Lydia, mostly items of silver and gold, had largely gone by the third century (and in Pausanias' day only a gift of Alyattes, a stand of welded iron that had once supported a silver bowl, yet remained), but the predominance among these early offerings of objects such as bowls, jars, tripods, shields and roasting-spits as well as decorative devices like the sphinx and the griffon may be contrasted with the later preference for anthropomorphic images. From the seventh and sixth centuries little sculpture in the round has been discovered, although we should not forget the bronze statuette in 'Dedalic' style (Room 2 of the Museum), the two monumental statues in marble said to be of Cleobis and Biton (Room 3) and the small bronze kouros, possibly an image of Apollo (Room 3). The Lydian kings, as we have seen, dedicated no statues either of Apollo or themselves. Only from the period of the Persian wars in the early fifth century do we find evidence of many statues dedicated in the likeness of Apollo, and until then there appears to have been almost no case of the dedication of a statue of a mere mortal. The golden statue of Alexander I of Macedon mentioned by Herodotos was among the first, and the Athenians also honoured Miltiades, the general at Marathon, with a portrait. However after the Persian wars a change came over the nature of many of the dedications, a change of emphasis towards the importance of the human form that to some extent corresponded with the development from the archaic style to the freer portraiture of the classical period.

Among the dedications of the classical period and afterwards, an important group was that of the athletes who had been victorious in the Games. Many victors gave statues of themselves 'ex-voto', as a result of a vow given to the god in the event of their success. The famous statue of the Charioteer (Room 12 of the Museum) was probably part of a bronze group dedicated by Polyzalos, ruler of Gela in Sicily (and the brother of Gelon of Syracuse), in thanks for his victory in th Pythian Games of 478 or 474 BC. It had stood a little above the temple until buried in the earthquake of 373 and would not have been seen by our Athenian. The Charioteer is scarcely an exact portrait, any more than a statue of a god might be a portrait, yet it is undoubtedly the image of a mortal. It exemplifies the principal elements in mature Greek art. Its calm beauty, the sense of restraint and the avoidance of the portrayal of emotion, is one strand. The other essential element, though a little muted in the heavily draped figure of the Charioteer, was the idealisation of the human form, the attempt to bring the human face and body to a state of divine-like perfection.

Statues of honour were particularly well-suited to this programme, since their purpose was precisely to glorify and immortalise the dead. The monument of Daochos II, which was dedicated not long after the battle of Chaironia and placed behind and above the monument of Gelon, is a good example (Room 11 of the Museum). Daochos, one of the rulers of Thessaly appointed by Philip of Macedon, and then one of his delegates to the Amphyctionic Council, had set up the series of nine marble statues, seven of which were of his dead forbears, the remaining two being of himself and his son. The most complete piece, which was probably a contemporary copy of a bronze statue by Lysippus, is that of the athlete Agias, a victor of the pancration at both Delphi and Olympia. No mortal could wish for a more complete apotheosis. The perfect form of the athlete, calm and at reast, remains full of a restrained vigour. The energy flows in alternating rhythms through the body from the thrust of the stance to the turn of the head so that the figure appears to be capable of almost any achievement.

The Greeks partly because of the view they enjoyed of their own capabilities could only imagine the gods in anthropomorphic form, and they went on to believe that men were capable of sharing on an appropriately reduced scale some of the divine attributes such as those of beauty and grace, strength and courage that were thought permanently to reside in the gods. If the sculptures on Greek temples and on the Delphic treasures tended to awaken awe at the power and might of the gods and heroes, the figures were never too remote that they might not be copied and their qualities imitated, and the great men whose statues adorned the sanctuaries and other public places represented those who if not in life then after death were shown as coming closest to this ideal. The Greek word for portrait was eikon, a word that has of course survived in reference to the portraits of the saints. In both cases the same tendency to idealisation has been at work. The only difference lies in the nature of the virtues portrayed.

10

THE ORACLE

The Pythia took her seat in the Temple of Apollo on the seventh day of each month when the god resided at Delphi. That day the Athenian presented himself at the temple. He was accompanied by the Athenian proxenos at Delphi who was to act as his sponsor. Earlier in the morning the two men had descended to the Castalian fountain to purify themselves in its water. After they had walked up again through the sanctuary the first duty was to make an offering on the large altar outside the temple. This consisted of a small cake of flour and honey mixed with olive oil and water, which the priests of Apollo provided, and for which an artificially high price was charged. In effect it was the charge for the coming consultation. There were several other enquirers including a Delphian, some Aetolians, several islanders and a dark Egyptian. From long tradition the Delphians had the right to consult the god first, and the Aetolians had lately enjoyed the privilege of entering after the Delphians. The order of the remaining consultants was then determined by lot as organised by the priests. Until his turn for the consultation of the Pythia should arrive the enquirer must wait outside the cella of the temple, in the shade of the peristyle.

The great temple at Delphi, of the Doric order and with forty-two columns in its peristyle, was only a little smaller than the Parthenon and dominated the sanctuary as much as the Temple of Athena commanded the Acropolis at Athens. The present building had been constructed in the later part of the previous century after the archaic temple built by the Alcmaeonids had been overthrown by an earthquake in 373. Contributions had come from throughout Greece, as for the previous temple, and the building programme included the construction of the large retaining wall to the north, the Ischegaon. The foundations of the earlier temple of dark Parnassos stone were reused, and new columns and entablature of tufa from Corinth and Sicyon had been imported to the port of Kirrha. The tufa was then covered with a white stucco of lime and powdered marble, polished and in some parts painted. The work had proceeded slowly. Owing to the disturbed political events of the fourth century, in particular the occupation of the sanctuary by

The Temple of Apollo

the Phocians and the Macedonian interventions, the building was not completed until almost the end of the century. However now it stood in all its splendour, with the colours still fresh upon the sculptures in the pediments.

On the east pediment facing the altar was portrayed the arrival at Delphi of Apollo, who was shown with his mother Leto, his sister the goddess Artemis and his companions the Muses. The same theme had adorned the east pediment of the archaic temple, the remains of which may be seen in Room 8 of the Museum. At the other end of the temple Dionysos occupied the centre of the pediment, while the Thyiads and the setting sun were also represented. Here the balance was struck between the two Delphic deities. However all the fourth century pedimental sculptures are lost except the figure (it is thought) of either Apollo or Dionysos displayed in Room 8 of the Museum.

Below the east pediment, in place of sculptural reliefs on the metopes, there hung the golden shields given to the previous temple by the Athenians from the spoils of the Persians and their Theban allies. It was the rededication of these shields in the new temple that had made the Thebans cause their allies the Amphissans to accuse the Athenians of impiety in the Amphictyonic Council, thus triggering the complicated events leading to the battle of Chaironia. They now glowed harmlessly enough in the mid-morning sun but to an Athenian who knew well the price of the freedom lost at Chaironia they lacked some of their lustre.

The day drew on. The Athenian waited under the shade of the columns as those ahead of him entered one by one into the interior of the temple. For the priests and the Pythia it involved a seemingly endless ritual, the preparations for which had begun shortly after dawn. At that early hour the priests had accompanied the Pythia to the Castalian. She was an old peasant woman who had only lately become the priestess of Apollo, but she had served the god all her life and knew what was expected of her. There at the spring they had ceremoniously purified themselves. Later, dressed in white robes and wearing a crown of laurel, the Pythia proceeded to the temple. On the hearth inside she burnt some laurel leaves and barley meal, again an act of ritual purification. Then she waited to enter the inner sanctuary until the priests had successfully offered a goat to Apollo. When the god had indicated his assent through the shivering of the animal, a process helped by the liberal use of cold water, the goat was sacrificed on the great altar outside. Only when the day had been declared auspicious for the consultation of the Pythia did she take her position in the sanctuary of the temple.

When his time arrived the Athenian straightaway entered the temple. The priests and the proxenos went with him, as well as a young slave leading a sheep intended for sacrifice at the hearth. The small procession passed into the fore-temple. This held the bronze statue of Homer and also the celebrated maxims of the seven sages which were inscribed on herms on either side of the inner doorway — 'Know thyself', 'Nothing too much' and, more to the taste of a merchant, 'Go surety and ruin is at hand'. Great wooden doors inlaid with ivory then led into the obscure light of the cella, the principal part of the temple and the home of the god.

Inside the cella, smoke from the meat still burning on the hearth from the previous victim rose lazily towards the openings under the roof where shafts of sunlight penetrated the gloom. The great room was divided into three aisles by two rows of columns and was filled with every kind of offering. There were tripods, statues and pieces of bronze armour shining dully in the shadows. From the fat rafters there hung the bay crowns of victorious athletes and even entire racing chariots. The walls had been painted with mythological scenes by Aristoclides, although these were already darkened by smoke and in the poor light they were difficult to see. There were several representations on the walls of the mysterious letter E, a symbol associated with Apollo, the meaning of which no one knew precisely. In the room there also stood images of the two Fates together with statues of Zeus and Apollo who were for once revealed as the Guides, and not the followers, of Fate. The great hearth with its perpetual fire of pine wood was in the centre, near the iron chair of Pindar where the poet by tradition had sat and composed his verses at Delphi.

The enquirer's first act was to sacrifice his victim upon the hearth which had now been cleaned of the blood from the previous slaughter. The sacrifice was an essential part of the ritual — and not only for the enquirer. The Delphians earned much of their living in this way. They had earlier sold the animal at the usual inflated price, and once it was slaughtered and a small part of the beast laid aside for the god to enjoy they were entitled to the rest, and this found its way into the shops and hotels of the city. It did not worry the Athenian too much. The Delphians had to make money in some way or another, and did not they themselves say that famine would be their lot were not the oracle and the pious their revenue?

With the sacrifice performed the Athenian was conducted towards the further end of the building where steps led down to a sunken area just over a metre below the level of the temple floor. On the left of this area was the true sanctuary, the adyton, while the right-hand part towards which he was walking was a kind of waiting room where the consultants waited to address the Pythia. He could look directly down into the sanctuary and for a moment he caught sight of the head of the Pythia where she sat upon the tripod, close to the branches of a straggling laurel tree. He could see too a large gold statue of Apollo holding a lyre (which the Phocians had not dared steal) and an ornate canopy covering the celebrated omphalos. However when the small party descended the steps to the waiting room, they lost sight of the adyton. The inner sanctuary was curtained across and the Pythia was no longer visible.

The chief priest, the prophitis, was standing in the small room and he beckoned the Athenian and his party to sit on the benches against the walls. From the adyton, behind the curtain, there was scarcely a sound except the rustling of the laurel leaves. The Athenian composed in his mind yet again the question he was to ask the oracle. As he did so he became aware of a sweet fragrance in the room, akin to incense but more delicate. At last the prophitis stepped forward, drew back the curtain and requested the enquirer to address his question to Apollo. The consultant stood up and quietly asked, 'To what gods or hero must I pray or sacrifice to obtain a son?'.

From the adyton and her seat on the tripod the Pythia looked directly at the consultant. She was shaking gently in one hand a freshly cut branch of bay. For some moments her eyes closed and her lips moved soundlessly as if she herself was speaking to the god, and then she gave her reply. It was brief, yet measured. The Athenian was directed to sacrifice two oxen and pray to the goddess Athena in her sanctuary at Delphi — the temple where he had paused on his way into the city. That was all, there was nothing further to be said. The prophitis drew the curtain across and the consultation was over.

The response was entirely, or almost entirely, satisfactory to our enquirer. By the nature of the oracle the birth of a son was not ruled out and the action prescribed was clear enough, even if the purchase of the oxen from the herds on the rich plain below would take the profits of his latest venture. He mounted the steps and without a backward glance walked out into the sunlight.

*

Was this then all — did consulting the oracle amount to no more than posing a simple question to an old woman seated behind a curtain? Certainly there were some additional elements, as we shall shortly see, but these were of more ritual than practical significance and should not be allowed to obscure the essential nature of what occurred, which depended ultimately on the faith of both the Pythia and the consultant that she was able to and did communicate the thoughts of Apollo.

We have seen that the Pythia was seated on a tripod, almost certainly upon the lid of its basin, which was thought to contain the bones of Python or Dionysos. Contact with the tripod was believed to be an essential prerequisite to the Pythia's ability to prophesy. The legs of the tripod may have stood over the mouth of a small artificial opening in the ground, made of masonry let into the earth, somewhat like the oracle of Trophonius. One tradition even suggested that Trophonius, who was also credited with building the first stone temple at Delphi, was responsible for such a structure. The chthonic associations of such a chasm in the earth, if it existed, are obvious. In one hand the Pythia held a branch of bay laurel (laurus nobilis, the sweet bay), a plant closely associated with Apollo and itself a symbol of purification. It is possible that the Pythia may have chewed some of the bay leaves, but if so this would have had little effect upon her as the bay has only culinary properties. Another ritual may have been to drink from a vessel which had been carried into the temple filled with the waters of the Cassotis, but this is only suggested in late authors like Pausanias. In fact the Pythia's seat upon the tripod and her holding of the bay were the only essential preliminaries for her performance in the adyton of which we can be sure. Even the fragrance described by Plutarch as sometimes filling the waiting room cannot have been of much significance. For although Plutarch speculates that the fragrance may have been an instance of the 'mantic spirit' by which he tried to explain the operation of the oracle, as a priest of Apollo he would have known if it was in any fundamental way related to the ritual of the priestess. The fragrance was probably no more than the occasional use of incense or some other scented spice.

No doubt the solemnity of the consultation was all the greater for its taking place not only in the innermost sanctum of the temple but among a number of objects of great sanctity. Some of these have been mentioned, including the tripod of Apollo and the cult statue of the god. There was also the famous omphalos, mentioned earlier. At one time the top of this conical stone was decorated with golden images of the two eagles of Zeus until they were stolen by the Phocians. The omphalos (a marble version of which has been discovered and placed in the Museum but is not the stone from the sanctuary) was one of the oldest objects at Delphi, and like the tripod was variously said to mark the resting place of either Python or Dionysos. The Greeks were not particularly systematic in their beliefs, any more than they are today, and there was also a stone block in the adyton similarly spoken of as the tomb of Dionysos. In addition the sanctuary was hung with sacred armour. All these things and indeed the many dedications in the megaron of the temple contributed to an atmosphere perhaps not unlike that of an Athonite church where the overpowering effect of one's surroundings may make sensation appear as belief even to the unbeliever.

In such an atmosphere the priestess, from a child the servant of Apollo, knew what was required of her, and the consultant was prepared to accept her replies as those of Apollo. There is no need for elaborate explanation of the Pythia's performance and now that only a small proportion of the recorded responses are thought to be genuine and those that are genuine appear to be limited to simple answers mostly on religious matters, such as cult foundations, festivals and prescriptions of sacrifices, there is less need than ever. It is not necessary to seek for caverns and mysterious vapours, of which there are and can be none, any more than we need to consider the chewing of laurel or the inhalation of hemp as sources of the Pythia's inspiration. Those modern pagans who for example speak of 'telluric forces' being fixed at Delphi by the killing of the Python and in some mysterious way influencing the Pythia are equally deluded; such forces are no more real than the immaterial exhalations mentioned by Plutarch. The reality is that the inspiration of the Pythia, sometimes described as 'enthusiasmos', was neither frenzy nor trance but was solely the inspiration of faith, or if you prefer superstition, and the remarkable fact is not that this is what occurred but the degree of success it enjoyed.

*

The oracle continued to function throughout antiquity answering the need for that direct communication with the supernatural which the Greeks craved. Of all the thousands of responses given only a fraction has survived and of that fraction there can be no absolute certainty of the authenticity of hardly a single one. It is doubtful if official records of oracles were kept at Delphi and the later transmission of the oracles, after they had been given, was only too likely to be the subject of distortion, not least by Delphi with a view to its own aggrandisement. Recent analysis of the surviving responses, by examining the characteristics of those recorded in near enough contemporary writers or inscriptions (and there are about seventy-five such 'historical' oracles), has suggested that these 'were pretty much confined to sanctions of laws and proposals, particularly on religious subjects, and to prescriptions of cult acts; and that exceptions, if any, were safe statements which anybody could make; but also that the response often had the same form as the question, which was expressed in one of two or three stereotyped forms. Not one can be considered an extraordinary utterance...There were no clever ambiguities, no revelations of the future in difficult language, no motives of the "first to be met" and "this will happen when such and such happens". No matter what the question, the oracle prescribed the foundation of a cult to states, the making of certain sacrifices to individuals; or it merely ratified plans already decided upon'.† Thus by these unromantic but realistic criteria almost all the remaining responses, including not only those given to Croesus but those given to the Athenians at the time of the invasion by Xerxes as well obviously all the oracles of legend such as those spoken to Laius and Oedipus, must either be rejected as not being genuine or be open to the gravest doubt. Moreover even the reputation acquired by Delphi later in antiquity for its important role in directing overseas colonisation during the archaic period is shown to be without historical foundation and merely the work of storytellers.

Owing to Greek credulity the reputation of Delphi depended at least as much on the oracles it had never given as on the more mundane responses it had. It was believed to be the truest of all oracles, and faith in its veracity could not be destroyed even when

†Fontenrose, *The Delphic Oracle* (1978), p. 42

on one occasion on the Pythia was alleged to have been bribed to give a favourable response. At some times the oracle enjoyed greater prestige than at others, depending upon the religious spirit of the period, but the exaggerated accounts of Delphi's oracular powers are themselves an indication of the generally high regard in which it was held. Moreover even if on a realistic assessment of Delphi's actual responses we must conclude that its impact on Greek affairs is much more limited than has often been thought, it cannot have been without its influence on the moral outlook of individuals in an otherwise amoral society.

Beyond its function as an oracle Delphi enjoyed a wider prestige as a Panhellenic sanctuary. We have seen how it came to be a repository for Greek art. In addition there were its festivals, and in particular the four-yearly Pythian Games, which ensured that Delphi remained a living religious centre where Greeks from different cities might meet together. Ancient authors speak of the importance to the Greeks of meeting at their sanctuaries to participate jointly in the festivals. This provided some counterpull to the centrifugal tendencies of the city-states. At Delphi this communal aspect had some specific, practical consequences. Beyond providing opportunities for discussion of troublesome disputes, the sanctuary was sometimes used for final arbitration upon these problems, and among the various inscriptions of public importance set up at Delphi there were many recording the boundaries established between cities. This accumulated prestige, resulting from its contributions in so many spheres, was then continually maintained by its friends and agents in many Greek cities, who were also able to keep the Delphic authorities informed of wider developments necessary to the proper function of the oracle.

Nonetheless paganism was not to endure for ever, and when it came to be replaced by a new religion from the East which distained such methods the oracle was bound to fail, since it could only be sustained on the beliefs of those around it. In the early part of the fourth century AD Constantine had legalised Christianity throughout the Roman Empire. When some thirty years later the Emperor Julian, who had apostatised from the Christian religion, sent his representative to Delphi and asked the oracle how he could restore the old glory to Apollo he received the last recorded reply of the Pythia. Whether or not genuine, the response is a poignant recognition of the departure of the god from the sanctuary before

even the prohibitions of Theodosios or the final destruction of the
temple of Arcadius:

> 'Tell ye the king: the carven hall is fallen in decay;
> Apollo hath no chapel left, no prophesying bay,
> No talking spring. The stream is dry that had so much to say.'

*

It remains to climb above the temple to the theatre and the
stadium, the principal places where the Pythian Games were
celebrated. The Pythian festival was first instituted as a funeral
celebration in memory of the death of Python; it was then held
every eight years and only consisted of a musical competition when
a hymn was sung in honour of Apollo to the accompaniment of the
cithara (a superior form of lyre). After the Sacred War and the
destruction of Kirrha the festival was reorganised by the
Amphictyony, and in keeping with the new status of the sanctuary
Games were now held on a large scale every four years, midway
between the Olympic festival. Within a few years all the athletic
competitions held at Olympia were included and some others (for
boys) even added. As befitted a god of music and the companion of
the Muses due emphasis was given to artistic events, with
competitions for the flute and cithara (the 'Pythian nomes'
illustrating in music the death of the Python), also for lyric poetry
and eventually for drama. The prize was a crown of laurel, as we
can see on the wall of the Athenian Treasury where wreaths
decorate the inscriptions of the names of victors, but the real
reward was the everlasting fame earned by a Pythian victory.

The Theatre was the scene of the performance of both the
dramatic and the lyrical competitions. It is reached by steps at the
western end of the Ischegaon, the retaining wall above the temple,
just beyond a large recess in the wall that once held a bronze group
by the sculptors Lysippos and Leochares representing Alexander
the Great being assisted in a lion hunt by the donor of the
monument, Crateros. The Theatre was built of local stone in the
fourth century, in effect completing the northwest corner of the
sanctuary, and could seat five thousand people. Almost two
thousand years after its construction its thirty-three tiers of seats
could still be seen when Cyriacus of Ancona visited Delphi in the
fifteenth century, but the entire Theatre was later covered with

earth. The 'stage', the structure at the rear of the orchestra, was probably deliberately kept low to prevent the view across the Pleistos gorge being obscured.

Before leaving the sanctuary enclosure we might briefly notice to the east of the Theatre and hard against the northern wall the scant remains of a quadrangular building which once contained some of the most remarkable paintings of antiquity. This was the Clubhouse dedicated by the inhabitants of Cnidos, a rectangular hall built of unburnt bricks with eight wooden columns on marble socles supporting the roof. A bench ran around the inside of the hall and it was a convenient meeting place for visitors to the sanctuary who could here sit and talk — indeed it is the scene of one of Plutarch's dialogues. Its fame rested on the paintings of the early fifth century artist Polygnotos, which covered all the interior walls, and of which Pausanias has left us such a detailed description that several plausible reconstructions have been attempted. To one side of the central entrance to the buidling Polygnotos had painted the capture of Troy and on the other the descent of Odysseus to the Underworld. Although we know the paintings survived into the fourth century AD, not a fragment of them now survives.

From the theatre a path leads through pine trees past the old Kerna spring up to the undreamt-of platform under the cliffs of Parnassos where the Stadium is situated, and where even today comparatively few people trouble to climb. In early spring the sandy soil that once knew the feet of athletes is covered with an unlikely carpet of green varied with countless wild hyacinths.

The Stadium was only placed here in the fifth century when the large supporting wall of polygonal masonry on the south was constructed. Until then it was situated in the plain of Crisa, perhaps near the hippodrome. For a long time after the Stadium was moved here the spectators probably had to be content with sitting on the bare earth or rocks around the track, as at Olympia, until the great Athenian benefactor Herodes Atticus furnished the stone seating in the second century AD. Its present appearance therefore dates from the Roman period, including the triumphal arches at the eastern end and the starting and finishing lines. On the north side there were twelve tiers of seats divided at intervals by gangways; in the middle there was a tribune for those officiating and in the northwest corner a vaulted fountain — the water from which would have been very welcome to spectators and athletes alike, since the Games took place in August. On the west and south there

The Stadium at Delphi

were only six tiers. In all the Stadium could seat some seven thousand people and embraced a running track 178 metres long, the length of a Roman stade. Here was held not only the foot races including the spectacular race in armour, but also the contests in boxing, wrestling and the pancration, as well as some of the musical performances.

That the Games should have been devoted to both athletic and artistic contests may be a little surprising to us, but the Greeks seem not to have subscribed to our quaint cultural distinctions. All the activities, since they were in honour of a god, were of equal worth and all were attempts to display human arete or ability to its utmost in whatever field was chosen for its exercise. Moreover the desire to develop a man's potential to the greatest possible degree, and a belief in the supreme powers of the gods, were entirely consistent — even complementary — attitudes within the Greek mind. The Greek deities, called into being to explain the works of nature, had for reasons connected both with the Greek personality and the subtle scale of the landscape been cast into the image of man. They always remained mysterious sources of power within nature and yet, as the projection of some of the most ideal of human qualities and being endowed with the best of human talents, they were still largely within human comprehension. As such, even if existing on a different level to man, the gods could be approached — they might be entreated through prayer and sacrifice and their intentions might be divined through auguries and oracles. But above all men might even attempt to emulate some of the qualities of the gods which by their very nature were the ideals of human behaviour.

One of the veins in Greek thought contemplated some possibility of communion with the gods after death. This was the teaching of the Eleusinian mysteries in particular. But the prevalent view, expressed in Homer, was that nothing except a gloomy, batlike existence faced the dead. Hence sprung the belief that while alive men must make use of all the capabilities they possessed. With no notion of sin and only little moral restraint on behaviour except the general principle that moderation was a virtue and excesses might be punished (although not invariably), it was inevitable that in many cases the unprincipled pursuit of one man's potential as conceived by his ambitions would only be at the cost of another man's position. This was especially true of political affairs. The competitive ethos which developed in the heroic age could (and frequently did) when pursued to its end lead to disaster, either in the case of individuals or even of whole cities. On the other hand the free scope for man's development also allowed him to attempt to rival the gods and to share in the better qualities attributed to them — their strength and beauty, their wisdom and temperance, and their gifts of poetry and art. This noble aim permeated some of the finest of the Greek achievement, which like that of the Middle Ages was largely religious in inspiration.

Yet the Greeks were realistic enough to know the imperfection and frailty of human effort, and alongside the triumphant belief in the potentiality of man there is concomitant pessimism, an almost existentialist appreciation of the purposefulness of life. 'Man's life is a day', wrote Pindar in a Pythian ode, 'What is he? What is he not? A shadow in a dream is man'. This melancholy chord can still sound even on the brightest summer day, when for a moment the colours become too intense and the world seems as brittle as glass.

*

Above the pine trees screening the stadium from the south can be seen on the far side of the Pleistos valley a path which winds up the face of Mount Cirphis. The carefully made track has fallen into disuse but once it led to the uplands of the village of Desphina which lies among fields of corn, hidden from sight. In the early summer the path through the fields towards the village is bordered by huge blue patches of wild delphinium sprinkled with poppies.

Galaxidi on the Gulf of Corinth

Far above the Stadium, on the hill of Philomelos where we may still see remains of the only fortifications ever attempted at Delphi, there are other prospects besides. Here, above the level of the Egyptian vultures which soar on black and white wings over the fields below, the view encompasses the pass to Boeotia and the mountains of the Peloponnese. Below you to the south, beyond the spur carrying the ruins of ancient Crisa, stretches the silvery plain which it once commanded, enclosed by the foothills of the Lidoriki mountains and the waters of the Bay of Itea. The white houses of Itea, the successor of all the ports in the gulf from prehistoric Kirrha to the Turkish Scala, straggle along the water's edge where the seafront is scattered with the sweet-smelling trees of the demotic song. On the far side of the bay, on a promontory, you see the once proud port of Galixidi, the ancient city of Chaleion, now sheltering memories of former times behind the brightly painted facades of its empty houses. Strung across the water between Galixidi and Itea are the small islands whose stories reach back into prehistory and which later provided refuge from the incursions of the Slavs and Bulgarians.

West of the Amphissan arm of the plain of Crisa, on a plateau below the Lidoriki summits, you look across to the cheese-producing village of Vinichora and at the houses of Ayia Evthymia situated near the ruins of the Locrian city of Myania. Out of sight on the flank of Parnassos, north of the village of Chriso, we may imagine high on a platform above the plain the Monastery of Prophitis Elias, at one time the rallying point for the revolutionary Panourias and now justly famous for the wooden screen carved in its church by the master Barba Nicolas. Further yet, at the head of the plain, guarding the pass to the north stands Amphissa, still dominated by the walls of its acropolis which later became the castle of the Frankish Autremencourts, and where in 1823 Byron was to have met Odysseus Androutsos.

Here then, where the history of Greece seems compressed into the confines of a single landscape, the road to Delphi is completed.

Appendix I

Travel Notes

HOW TO REACH THE PARNASSOS AREA

From Athens
By car: either by National Highway 1 which you turn off north of Thebes for Levadia and Delphi (3 hours) or by a slightly longer but more attractive route over Mount Cithairon from Elevsis to Thebes, then Levadia and Delphi (3½ hours).

By bus: from the terminal at 260 Liossion Street (known as 'Tris Yefires'). To reach the terminal take a taxi or bus No. 24 from Amalias Avenue outside the National Gardens — allow at least half an hour, longer at midday. Buses run direct to Levadia (2 hours), Arachova, Delphi (3½ hours), Amphissa, Itea and Galaxidi. The frequency depends upon the destination: for example a bus runs about hourly to Levadia, five to six times daily to Delphi and twice a day to Galaxidi. There is one bus a day to Osios Loukas, but it only allows 1½ hours there before returning. (Some tours include Osios Loukas on the way to Delphi). Bus times from the National Tourist Office in Syntagma Square (Tel: 3222.545). It is always wise to arrive in good time at the terminal, as the buses get full.

By train: from Station Larissas which is quickly reached by bus (yellow bus No.1 from Syntogma or blue bus No. 847 from Menandrou, near Omonia) or taxi and is about 15 minutes walk from Omonia. The booking office is at 6 Sina, off Akadimias (Tel: 3624.402). Trains go to the stations at Levadia (2 hours), Davlia, Tithorea and Amphiclia; there are four to five a day to Levadia, fewer to the others. All the stations are some distance outside the places they serve; at Levadia there is a bus connection, otherwise you will have to take a taxi or walk.

From Patras and the Peloponnese

The quickest ferry across the Corinthian Gulf is between Rion and Antirrion (very frequent). A good road runs along the north coast of the gulf between Navpactos and Itea (1½ hours), and the bus from Patras connects at Navpactos with the bus to Itea, Delphi, etc. There is now also a ferry five or six times a day from Aigion to Ayios Nikolaos.

TRAVEL WITHIN THE REGION

West from Levadia
In addition to the through buses on the routes between Levadia and Itea or Amphissa which you can also take for local journeys there are local buses on the same routes. Enquire at the practoreio or agency in Odhos Kaliankaki, Levadia (situated just below the central plateia); the agency serves all the towns and villages within the nome of Boeotia.

Distomo-Anticyra: fairly frequent buses.

Distomo-Osios Loukas: two buses a day (early morning and early afternoon).

Itea-Amphissa: very frequent service. Most buses begin and end their journeys in Kirrha.

Itea-Desphina: two to three buses a day.

Itea-Galaxidi: two to three buses a day.

Cephisos Valley
From Leviada (the agency in Odhos Kaliankaki) there are buses to most of the villages in this area, such as Chaironia, Ayios Vlasios, Davlia, Ayia Marina, Tithorea and Amphiclia. Frequency varies from place to place, but generally there is usually a bus in the morning, at lunchtime and in the evening — though the last bus may not return until the next morning and then you must either visit in the morning or stay the night (see below) or take a taxi. Amphiclia-Gravia: fairly frequent buses, which stop at the villages of Polidrosos and Lilaia. From the village of Lilaia a bus goes three times a week to Eptalophos.

Parnassos
There are no buses on the road between Eptalophos and Arachova.

ACCOMMODATION
Apart from the obvious places like Levadia, Arachova, Delphi, Itea and Galaxidi (each of which has at least two hotels — and Delphi has many times that number — and also several adequate restaurants) you can stay the night and find a meal at Distomo (two hotels), Amphiclia (hotel), Amphissa (hotel), Tithorea (rooms), Davlia (rooms) and Eptalophos (rooms). Sometimes it may be difficult to find a midday meal in some of the villages. At Osios Loukas it is no longer possible to stay the night, but there is a

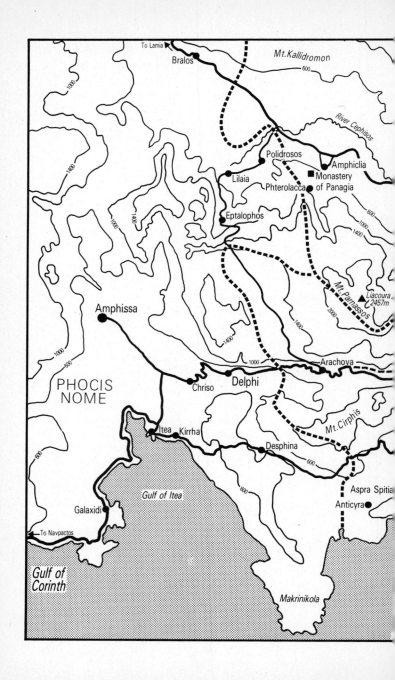

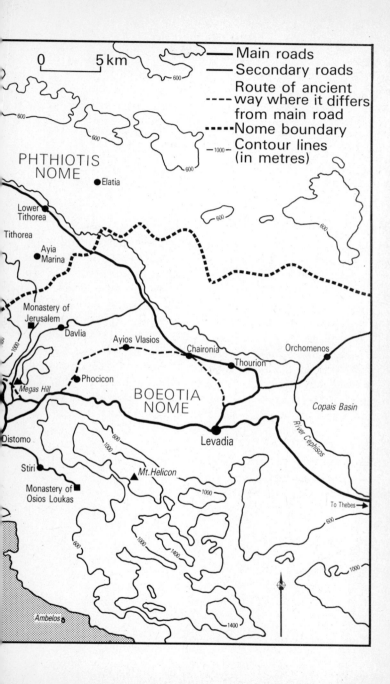

restaurant open at midday. There is a youth hostel at 29 Apollonos, Delphi.

CAMPING
There are two campsites with the usual facilities below Delphi on the road to Itea, another at Chriso, and two more east of Itea on the road for Desphina. You can also camp at Galaxidi.

SWIMMING
There is good swimming at Kirrha, Itea, Galaxidi and points west. The bay of Anticyra is beautiful enough but said to be polluted by the aluminium factory.

PARNASSOS
Climbing: for use of the refuge 'Sarantari' (1900 metres) and other information contact the Greek Alpine Association, 68 Aeolou, Athens (Tel: 321.2429). The guide in Arachova was last known to be N Georgakos (Tel: 31.391).

Skiing: there are two principal areas, the Athens Ski Club (24 kilometres from Arachova: for information Tel: 0267.31391) and the National Tourism Organisation Ski Centre (27 km from Arachova and also reached from Amphiclia via Phterolacca) which is a newer venture with better facilities. The NTO Ski Centre has an office near the Xenia hotel in Arachova: for information Tel: 0267.31692. Private transport is necessary to both areas. Accommodation can be found at Arachova or Amphiclia.

WALKING
The following walks can be recommended:
Levadia-Chaironia (p.45) 2 hours
Chaironia-Ayios Vlasios (p.64) ¾ hour
Ayios Vlasios-Davlia (p.69) 1¾ hours
Ayios Vlasios-Keresi (p.69) 1 hour
Davlia-Keresi (p.71) 1½ hours
Davlia-Tithorea (p.119) 2½ hours
Tithorea-Amphiclia (p.132) 2 hours
Amphiclia-Polidrosos (p.135) 1½ hours
Polidrosos-ruins of Lilaia (p.136) 1½ hours
Lilaia-Eptalophos (p.138) 1½ hours
Eptalophos-Corycian Cave (p.139) 4 hours
Delphi-Corycian Cave (p.139, 144) 3 hours

Delphi-Desphina (p.180) 3 hours
Climb to summit of Parnassos (p.116) 2½ hours minimum

MUSEUMS AND SITES

Delphi: the Sanctuary of Apollo is open 8am to 6.45pm every day except for Sundays and holidays when the hours are 8am to 5.45pm; the museum is open 8.45am to 3pm every day except for Sundays and holidays when the hours are 10am to 3pm. It is closed on Tuesdays.

Osios Loukas: open 8am to 7pm every day except for Sundays and holidays when it opens 9am to 7pm.

Chaironia museum: open 9am to 1pm and 4pm to 6pm except Tuesdays.

Appendix II

Osios Loukas: Principal Decoration

1 Christ
2 Mother of God
3 St John the Baptist
4 St Gregory the Theologian
5 St Athanasios
6 St Theodore of Tyre
7 St Silvester
8 St Achilios
9 St Spyridon
10 St Cyprian
11 St Anthimos
12 St Elevtherios
13 St Polycarpos
14 St Antipas
(below, the prophet Daniel and the Three Holy Infants)
15 St Gregory of Nisa
16 St Philotheos
17 St Hierotheos
18 St Dionysios the Areopagite
19 St Cyril of Alexandria
20 St Gregory the Armenian
21 St Ignatios
22 St Klimis
23 missing
24 St Avxentios
25 St Vincent
26 St Victor
27-31 missing
32 St Theodore of Tyre
33 St Nestor
34 St Demetrios
35 St Procopios
36 St Christopher
37 St Mercury
38 St George
39 St Nicholas the Young
40 missing
41 Mother of God
42 St Pandeleimon
43 Christ
44 Archangel Uriel
45 St Zacharias
46 Archangel Raphael
47 St Jason
48 St Sosipater
49 St Cleopas
50 St Ananias
51 Mother of God
52 St Luke the Stirite
53 Christ
54 Archangel Michael
55 St Jacob the brother of God
56 Archangel Gabriel
57 St Nicanor
58 St Silas, next to St Timothy
59 St Prochoros
60 St Stephen
61 St Barnabas
62 St John Chrysostom, below the Mother of God and St Anna
63 St Nicholas
64 St Gregory the Wonder-Worker
65 St Basil
66 St Adrian
67 St Triphon
68 St Agathangelos
69 St Nicetas
70 St Theodosios
71 St Savvas
72 St Pachomios
73 St Evthymios
74 St Abramios
75 St John the Kalivite
76 St Pimin
77 St John Kolovos
78 St Stephen the Young
79 St Martinianos
80 St Nicon the Penitent
81 St John Klimakos
82 St Makarios the Egyptian
83 St Anthony
84 St Ephraim
85 St Arsenios
86 St Ilarion
87 St Nilos
88 St Dorotheos
89 St Theoctistos
90 St Maximos
91 St Sisios
92 St Ioannikios
93 St Theodore Studitis
94 St Daniel
95 St Luke Gournikiotis

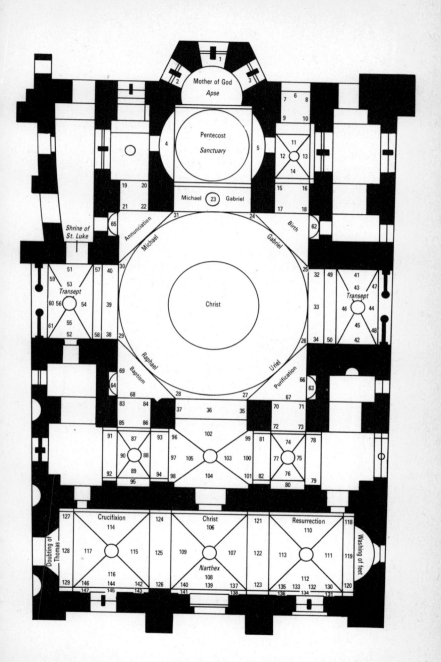

96–105 missing
106 Mother of God
107 Archangel Gabriel
108 St John the Baptist
109 Archangel Michael
110–113 missing
114 St Kosmas
115 St Cyros
116 missing
117 St John
118 St Thomas
119 St Bartholomew
120 St Philip
121 St Paul
122 St Jacob
123 St John the Theologian
124 St Peter
125 St Mark
126 St Andrew
127 St Matthew

128 St Simon
129 St Luke
130 St Thekla
131 St Anastasia
132 St Constantine
133 St Elena
134 St Petronia
135 St Agatha
136 St Evgenia
137 St Pigasios
138 St Anembodistos
139 St Akindinos
140 St Aphthonios
141 St Elpidophoros
142 St Irene
143 St Evphymia
144 St Ekaterina
145 St Marina
146 St Barbara
147 St Juliana

Appendix III

Delphi Museum

LAYOUT: PRINCIPAL EXHIBITS

Landing: ancient copy in marble of the omphalos; seventh century BC bronze cauldron with tripod; first century AD marble frieze from the theatre.

Room 1: the first case on the left includes Mycenaean idols in female form from the areas of the Sanctuary of Athena Pronaia and the Sanctuary of Apollo (1400–1100 BC), also Mycenaean vases from the cemeteries of Delphi; the first case on the right has Geometric vases from Delphi (900–700 BC), while the furthest case in the middle of the room has Geometric idols of the same period from the Sanctuary of Apollo.

Room 2: bronze shields, and bronze griffin heads from a cauldron once supported by a tripod, all of the seventh century BC; seventh century BC bronze statuette of a young man in 'Dedalic' style; sixth century BC bronze statuette of Apollo.

Room 3: two monumental statues in marble from the early sixth century BC probably of the Argive heroes Cleobis and Biton; five metopes from the Sicyonian treasury of the mid-sixth century BC, the best preserved showing Castor, Pollux and Idas plundering cattle, and the Calydonian Boar.

Room 4: archaic silver bull (reconstructed) of the sixth century BC and remains of parts of at least three chryselephantine statues of the same period from the deposit discovered in 1939 in front of the Stoa of the Athenians; bronze incense burner of fifth century BC.

Room 5: decoration from the Siphnian Treasury (c525 BC), including most of its frieze of Parian marble, the finest of which is the northern side showing the war of the gods and the giants and the eastern showing the gods watching the fighting in the Trojan War; also part of the eastern pediment which showed the quarrel over the Pythia's tripod between Apollo and Heracles; the upper part of one of the two Caryatids that supported the front of the treasury, and remains of the lotus and palmette decoration of the doorway; there is also the Naxian Sphinx of about 570 BC.

Room 6: the twenty-four remaining metopes in Parian marble from the Athenian Treasury (c490 BC) showing the battle between the

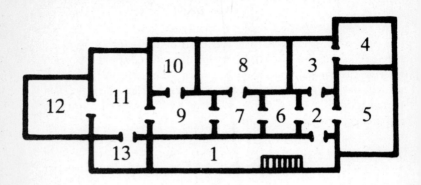

Athenians and the Amazons, the feats of Theseus, and the labours of Heracles — among the best preserved are the contest of Theseus with the Amazon queen Antiope, Theseus and the bull of Marathon, Theseus killing the Minotaur, and Heracles with the Hind of Ceryneia.

Room 7: the remains of the western pediment from the archaic Temple of Apollo in stone, showing the battle of the gods and giants; two *Hymns to Apollo* from the second century BC which were inscribed on the walls of the Athenian Treasury complete with musical notes.

Room 8: the remains of the eastern pediment from the archaic temple in marble given by the Alcmaeonid family, which showed the arrival of Apollo at Delphi with Artemis and Leto; four inscription steles from the second part of the fourth century BC with accounts concerning the rebuilding of the temple after its destruction by earthquake in 373 BC and with records of the fines paid by the Phocians following their thefts from the sanctuary during the Phocian War; statue of Dionysos or possibly Apollo from the western pediment of the fourth century temple.

Room 9: fifth century BC funerary stele of an athlete; round altar from the Sanctuary of Athena Pronaia with a frieze of young girls (first century BC).

Room 10: part of the restored entablature of the fourth century Tholos in the Sanctuary of Athena with four fragmentary metopes which probably portrayed the war of the Amazons and the War of the Centaurs.

Room 11: sculpture of the fourth century BC, including the acanthus column set up by the Athenians which once supported a tripod with three women, probably Thyiads, dancing around it, and the offering of the Thessalian Daochos II dedicated shortly after the battle of Chaironia — of the original nine statues in marble six now survive on the original base, the most complete being that of the athlete Agias, a victor in the Games, which was probably a contemporary copy of a bronze statue by Lysippus; the statue of an old man from the third century BC.

Room 12: the Charioteer of about 475 BC, probably once part of a bronze group dedicated by Polyzalos the ruler of Gela in Sicily in thanks for his victory in the Pythian Games and later buried in the earthquake of 373 BC.

Room 13: a marble statue of the second century AD of Antinoos the favourite of the Emperor Hadrian; the furthest case on the left has objects of the archaic and classical periods discovered in the Corycian Cave where they were dedicated to Pan and the Nymphs.

Appendix IV

The Sanctuary of Apollo

1 Base from bronze bull dedicated by the Corcyraeans c480 BC.

2 Base for nine statues dedicated by Arcadians post-369 BC

3 ?Spartan monument of thirty-seven statues dedicated after the victory over the Athenians in 404 BC

4 Base of Trojan Wooden Horse set up by the Argives after their victory over the Spartans in 414 BC

5 Athenian monument dedicated after Marathon (490 BC)

6 Argive monument of Seven Against Thebes dedicated after their victory over the Spartans in the mid-fifth century BC

7 Argive monument of Sons of Seven Against Thebes dedicated same time as 6

8 Argive monument of heroes and kings of Argos dedicated after the foundation of Messene in 369 BC

9 Treasury of Sicyon c500 BC

10 Treasury of Siphnos c525 BC

11 Treasury of the Boeotians

12 Treasury of Megara

13 Treasury of the Athenians post-490 BC

14 Treasury of Syracuse post-413 BC

15 Delphian Council House

16 Rock of the Sybil

17 Naxian Sphinx c570 BC

18 ?Stepterion

19 Stoa of the Athenians post-480 BC

20 Polygonal wall of the sixth century BC

21 Treasury of Corinth, mid-seventh century BC

22 Base of monument of Plataia post-479 BC

23 Base of gold chariot dedicated by the Rhodians

24 Chian altar dedicated in the early fifth century BC

25 Offering of Gelon tyrant of Syracuse and his three brothers after Himera (480 BC)

26 ?Acanthus column dedicated by the Athenians in the fourth century BC

27 Base of Apollo Sitalcas

28 Base of bronze palm tree dedicated by the Athenians after the battle of Eurymedon (468 BC)

29 Pillar of Prusias, king of Bithynia, second century BC

30 Cassotis fountain

31 Monument of Daochos II, fourth century BC

32 Shrine of Neoptolemos

33 Portico built by Attalos I, King of Pergamon, third century BC

34 Temple of Apollo (fourth century BC)

35 Ischegaon, retaining wall built after earthquake of 373 BC

36 Crateros monument dedicated post-320 BC

38, 39 ?Shrines of Dionysos

40 Cnidian Clubhouse, fifth century BC

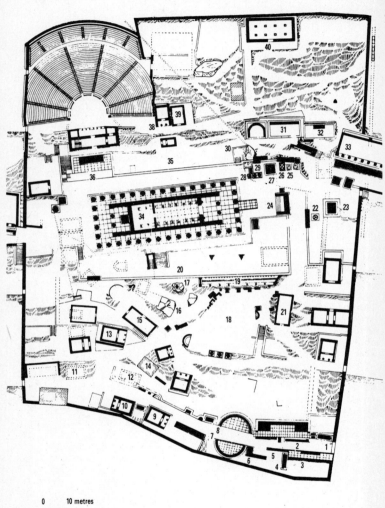

0   10 metres

Appendix V

Outline Chronology

Neolithic Age		from c6000 BC
Bronze Age	Early Helladic	c2800–2000 BC
	Middle Helladic	c2000–1600 BC
	Late Helladic (Mycenaean)	c1600–1100 BC
Iron Age commences	Dorians arrive	c1100 BC
	Archaic Period	from c750 BC
	Classical Period	from c500 BC
	Hellenistic Period	from c323 BC
	Roman Greece	from c146 BC
	Byzantine Greece	from c395 AD
	Fall of Constantinople to the Turks	1453
	Turkish Greece	from c1456
	War of Independence	1821–1832

Select
Bibliography

An asterisk indicates that the work is in Greek.

Chandler R, *Travels*, London 1817
Clarke E, *Travels*, London 1818
Dakin D, *British and American Philhellenes*, Thessaloniki 1955
Dakin D, The Greek Struggle for Independence 1821–1833, Batsford 1973
*Dalkas E, *St Luke and his Monastery*, Athens 1978
Diehl C, *L' Eglise et les Mosaiques du Convent de Saint-Luc*, Paris 1968
Dodwell E, *Tour through Greece*, London 1819
Fermor P L, *Roumeli*, John Murray 1966
Finlay G, *History of Greece 146 BC to AD 1864*, Oxford 1877
Fontenrose J, *The Delphic Oracle*, University of California Press 1978
Frazer J G, *Commentary on Pausanias*, London 1898
Gell W, *Itinerary of Greece*, London 1827
Gordon T, *History of the Greek Revolution*, Edinburgh 1832
Hoyle P, *Delphi*, Cassell 1967
*Kouphou I N, *Greek Demotic Songs*, Athens 1970
*Lappas T, *Arachova*, Athens 1961
*Lappas T, *Levadia*, Athens 1954
*Lappas T, *Levadia and Levadites in '21*, Athens 1971
*Lappas T, *Roumeliots in the Revolution (Isaias, Logothetis and Bousgos)*, Athens 1944
Lawrence A W, *Greek Aims in Fortification*, Oxford University Press 1979
Lawson J C, *Modern Greek Folk-Lore and Ancient Greek Religion*, Cambridge 1910
Leake W M, *Travels in Northern Greece*, London 1835
Leekly D and Efstratiou N, *Archaeological Excavations in Central and Northern Greece*, Noyes Press 1980
Matthews K, *Memories of a Mountain War*, Longman 1972
Mure W, *Journal of a Tour of Greece*, London 1842
*Papachatzas N, *Commentary on Pausanias*, Athens 1969
Parke H W, *Greek Oracles*, Hutchinson 1967
Parke H W and Wormell D E W, *The Delphic Oracle*, Oxford 1956

Pausanias, *Description of Greece*, translated by WHS Jones, Loeb Classical Library 1935

*Politis N, *Demotic Songs of the Klephts*, Athens 1914

Poulsen F, *Delphi*, London 1920

Roux G, *Delphes: son oracle et ses Dieux*, Paris 1976

Runciman St, *Byzantine Style and Civilisation*, Penguin 1975

St Clair W, *That Greece Might Still be Free*, Oxford 1972

St Clair W, *Trelawny the Incurable Romancer*, John Murray 1977

Schultz R W and Barnsley S H, *The Monastery of St Luke of Stiris*, London 1901

Scranton R L, *Greek Walls*, Harvard 1941

Spon J, *Voyage*, Amsterdam 1679

Trelawny E, *Records of Shelley, Byron and the Author*, London 1878

Tozer H F, *Lectures on the Geography of Greece*, John Murray 1873

Wace A J B and Thompson M S, *The Nomads of the Balkans*, Methuen 1914

Ware T, *The Orthodox Church*, Penguin 1972

Wheler G, *Journey into Greece*, London 1682

Woodhouse C M, *The Philhellenes*, Hodder and Stoughton 1969

Index

Italicised page numbers denote entries in the Appendices